The Sanity Inspectors

The Sanity Inspectors

Friedrich Deich

Translated from German by Robert Kee

Introduction by Sinclair McKay
Afterword by Chris Maloney

RECOVERED BOOKS
BOILER HOUSE PRESS

Contents

3

Introduction
by Sinclair McKay

9

The Sanity Inspectors
*by Friedrich Deich and translated
from German by Robert Kee*

277

Afterword: Being Disagreeable
by Chris Maloney

Introduction

by Sinclair McKay

'Aren't truth and error really just dependent on what the majority of people happen to think?' asks the naïve hero Robert Vossmenge near the start of this story. Yet when an entire society is in the grip of a murderous set of beliefs, how might individuals retain their own moral foundations? In *The Sanity Inspectors*, this fascinating novel by Friedrich Deich first published in Germany in 1955, we are shown – through the eyes of an idealistic (and, as he considers himself, eminently rational) young psychiatrist – various cases of mental breakdown while outside the doors of his institution a nation descends into the darkness of Nazism. What makes the book so compelling now is not just its clarity and vividness, but also its gravity-defying lightness of touch. The weightiest questions of goodness and evil, sanity and madness, agency and helplessness, are conjured through a series of episodes and vignettes, a wide range of intriguing psychiatric encounters that occasionally anticipate Joseph Heller's *Catch-22*.

One of the enduring – and it seems unsolvable – enigmas of the Nazi years is just how complete their command of the national consciousness was. Genetics; eugenics; racial purity; the final solution. What made this nauseously fast progression into mass murder possible? Even in 1933, as Hitler assumed power and the state brought Jew-hatred into law, how many Gentile citizens felt that it was regrettable yet necessary? *The Sanity Inspectors* is one of those works of German fiction – others include Erich Kastner's earlier *Going To The Dogs*, published in 1931, which queasily observed the growing prevalence of Nazi street violence, and Heinz Rein's *Berlin Finale*, dealing with the final infernal days of the Battle of Berlin and published in 1947 – that shine a light into Nazi Germany's most terrible moral fogs.

As it opens, *The Sanity Inspectors* carries little hint of the darkness to come. Its narrative is concentrically arranged based on Vossmenge's papers and follows his increasingly fraught professional life from Weimar Germany to the Nazi supremacy and the fires of war in the Mediterranean. Voss-menge is in some ways an idealist seen standing at an angle to orthodoxy; whether dealing with cases of schizophrenia or mistaken diagnoses, he has a constant need to interrogate prevailing clinical assumptions.

And early on, his key encounters with the hospital Pastor Kurt Degenbrück, and that man's firm, clear-eyed religious faith, bring a fascinating new depth to questions of the mind, of consciousness, of the soul. Both men will have their lives wrenched to and fro in the traumatic years that follow. Their discussions and debates – sharp, astringent, mutually sceptical yet touched with rough affection, 'ice-cold' psychiatric reason pitted against the passionate church – start to throw fresh light on the darkening moral landscape around them. These exchanges, sometimes in epistolatory form, are fast and exhilarating. Dr Vossmenge at one point demands of the Pastor what he would do if a child of his were to contract diptheria: seek a doctor – or pray to God? Degenbrück's swift answer via telegram is wittily impatient: 'You ass stop I'd do both.' Later, the Pastor forces Vossmenge to look more closely at the eugenic rationale for the Nazi campaign of sterilisation of 'imbeciles': who defines such scientific categories, and who judges who fits within them? And at what point does the term imbecility widen to become a death sentence on all?

At the outset of Hitler's regime, Vossmenge is denied membership of the Nazi Party for the unpardonable crime of a joke. 'Of course,' as one colleague declares at a public meeting, 'all Jews could be sent to some island where they would all be together. But what is then to be done about the people who are only partly Jewish?' Vossmenge shouts: 'They could be sent to a peninsula'. His superior is also banned from joining the Party. Why? 'I laughed.'

Seeking to elude hostile party apparatchiks, Vossmenge joins the Luftwaffe as a medical officer, first in North Africa and then in the anarchy of the slow retreat through Italy. The shadow line between insanity and rationality is crossed frequently by military commanders. Here, amid blood and death, the bitterest of human comedies plays out. Both Vossmenge and Degenbrück – as men who see clearly and who cannot resist the impulse to speak the truth aloud – will find themselves being pulled ever closer to the maelstrom of mortality.

What makes this story all the more remarkable is the novel's direct readability. There is something here of the colourful cleverness – the paradoxes and intellectual cartwheels – to be found in G. K. Chesterton's Father Brown stories (where theology and fashionable scientific assumptions were also in frequent conflict). Obviously, this is all written by Deich in hindsight, yet the questions that the narrative raises about conscience and about the power of individual actions, haunt the imagination. How far was it possible for intelligent people to believe that the intense cruelty of Nazism was somehow a natural function of the state? This question – concerning open violence and oppression and even torture within the public realm – can be applied in different cases today, across the world. If the majority of people believe something is true, how can the few unbelievers tell them otherwise?

In the immediate post-war years, there arose a German genre of Trümmerfilm ('rubble films'): dramas set amid the bloodied dust of smashed cities. *The Sanity Inspectors* depicts a world where the rubble is intellectual. 'I can never forgive myself that I have done nothing to oppose the inhuman cruelties of this authoritarian regime,' says Vossmenge at his last meeting with Pastor Degenbrück. 'On the other hand, though, I don't see what one could have done to combat the madness of our time.' Movingly, the Pastor gives him absolution: *'Ego te absolve in nominee Patris et Filii et Spiritus Sancti.'* Yet can this conceivably be extended to wider German society? There has to be atonement, not just for individual fictional characters but on the part of a real populace that was led into the foulest darkness. Fiction such as this is not by itself atoning, but it gingerly raises the question of millions of individual consciences and how they were to face the many millions more of terrifying, squalid murders carried out in their name.

The Sanity Inspectors

*by Friedrich Deich and translated
from German by Robert Kee*

Introduction

/\

During the last war the famous villa d'Este on the shores of Lake Como was turned into a hospital for the German air force. It was there that a court martial set me a difficult task: I had to give my professional opinion on an officer of the medical corps who was of the same rank as myself and like me a psychiatrist. This task of sitting in judgment as one psychiatrist on another, of revealing as it were a cross section of his state of mind, assessing his motives and giving some picture of the different sides of his personality presented me with an almost insoluble problem. A thorough enquiry of this sort into a person's whole mental structure involves the use of a number of questions which may give a clue to the clinical symptoms in his psychological condition. But when the subject of the enquiry is himself a psychiatrist, he sees through all such questions at once. In this case the usual roles were reversed. My patient had to submit to an endless series of questions which he was more accustomed to put himself, and this caused him to set up an insuperable barrier of mistrust. So, he proposed that he should be allowed to put his thoughts down on paper. In fact, this remedy saved us both some painful moments for we would otherwise have been forced to admit that psychiatry is of limited value when the patient himself is master of its secrets.

The prisoner's name was Robert Vossmenge, a Major in the medical corps, and he was sent to our hospital under strong escort. The crime of which he was accused entailed a serious penalty. To ensure that its verdict should be a just one the court martial ordered him to be put under mental observation for a period of six weeks.

The Villa d'Este lies right on Lake Como itself in a wonderful park laid out with fountains. On the north this park is bounded by a sheer cliff which falls straight to the lake below. Perched on the top of this cliff is a long narrow building which at one time was occupied by the servants of the owner of the villa. When the magnificent villa was turned into a hotel for rich Americans to spend the summer in, this eyrie was used to house the hotel staff. The long narrow corridor on the first floor ended in a charming little room from which there was a superb view over Lake Como and the neighbouring mountains. And it was in this room that Doctor Robert Vossmenge sat, a candidate for death, and wrote out the story of his life. In the course of six weeks he covered several hundred sheets of paper. And day and night a military policeman stood guard outside his door.

From what he wrote, and from certain letters and other notes, I put together an extensive dossier which I handed over to the court martial. These papers were destroyed at the end of the war. But I had a copy of them which Robert Vossmenge had made over to me just before his death. He expressly promised me the rights of publication. The book which follows consists of extracts from this dossier which I managed to save from the hazards of war and life in a prison camp. Without substantially altering the personal style of the narrator I have arranged the material chronologically and in its context. Where certain chapters seemed to need linking by some explanatory remarks of my own, I have added these in italics.

Chapter 1

/\

The old lady lay quietly in her bed until lunch-time. Then she got up, helped the sister carry lunch in for the patients, collected up the plates when the meal was over and in her quiet friendly way offered to help with the washing-up. Throughout the morning she was just a sweet lovable little old lady, polite and friendly to everyone, and possessed of a simple irresistible charm. The patients in the women's ward all loved her. Even those who remained entirely wrapped up in themselves when the doctor came on his rounds and hadn't so much as a glance to spare for him—the mentally ill are usually interested only in themselves and not in the outside world—even they would show by the benevolence of their expression that they were aware of her presence.

It was after lunch that the old lady became restless. She kept on going over to the window and peering out into the street, as if she were expecting someone. Then she started rattling the ward doors, searching in vain for the handle—there are no door handles in mental hospitals—and finally shuffled over to the sister on duty.

'Sister dear,' she said softly, not wishing to disturb the patients during their rest. 'Sister dear, my son is being kept a prisoner in the cellar. They're torturing him there.'

'Lie down, Frau Professor, you'll soon feel better,' said the sister without looking up from her sewing.

'I'm quite all right, thank you,' said the old lady. Her husband had been a Professor at Konigsberg. He had been dead for years. 'But it's my poor son, you see. They're torturing him.'

Then she ran across to the doors which separated the ward from the surgery. She knocked gently.

'Doctor, dear! My poor son!'

But there was no sign of life behind the door. There was never anyone there at lunch-time. Gradually the knocking became more insistent.

'Doctor, dear! Help! My son is imprisoned in the cellar. They're torturing him. They'll kill him.'

The ward doctor, Dr Stöhr, went on his rounds about four o'clock. I was then the youngest assistant in the clinic and had just been attached to the women's ward.

He turned to me and said:

'This'll give you the right idea of psychiatry! Now up goes the curtain. *William Tell* Act 4 Scene 3. Gessler and. Rudolf von Harras disclosed in an empty street.'

Quickly he unbarred the doors which lead into the ward.

The Frau Professor rushed straight at us. She knelt down in front of us and began wringing her hands.

'Doctor, dear, my poor son! They're torturing him! They're killing him with sticks and stones. Go down to the cellar and help him or he'll die!'

'Ah! Frau Professor!' said the doctor genially, 'And how are we to-day?' He turned to me and added: 'It's the same thing every day. I'm getting fed up with it.'

'I'm very well thank you, doctor,' said the old lady, 'but it's my son. They're torturing him. Please go down to the cellar.'

'Your son sends you his love. He's written to say that he's in the best of health,' said Dr Stöhr, and then turning to me again: 'Schizophrenia, personality unaffected, always friendly. She hears her son crying out and thinks he's being tortured down in the cellar where the boilers are. The hallucinations get worse towards evening. Nothing much we can do. Some bromide, skopolamin at nights.'

He turned to one of the other patients and took no more notice of the old lady. She followed us at a respectful distance, plucking us by the sleeve from time to time.

'Doctor, dear! Don't forget to go down to the cellar, will you? My poor son!'

When Dr Stöhr had finished his rounds and was back in the surgery again, he sighed.

'The psychiatrist's job isn't an easy one. I want to help my patients, but there's a limit to what I can do for them. Sometimes I wonder why I didn't become a surgeon. The surgeon wins his battles with the knife. But it's a bloody business, surgery. Not my line. We psychiatrists are more civilised: we keep our hands clean.'

He looked at himself complacently in the mirror. I said nothing.

'Besides, psychiatry's a fascinating science,' went on Dr Stöhr. 'It concerns itself with the very stuff of human existence. Analysing a mind is something altogether different from amputating a leg or testing urine. Even an aged schizophrenia of this sort has something of the splendour and tragedy of life about it. A mother thinks her son is being tortured. Her hallucination is identical with the medieval concept of hell. We say that her madness is isolated. Apart from this one particular delusion she's as sane as any of us. What's the cause of it all? What is mental illness anyway? In another age we would have said that the old lady was possessed of a devil. But we don't believe in devils any more now so we can't express her state of mind visually at all.'

'Here she is again,' I said.

There was a gentle knocking at the door.

'Doctor, dear, they're torturing him. They're smashing him to pieces! They're killing him! Please go down to the cellar!'

The knocking was more emphatic and the old lady's voice sounded more desperate than before.

'We'll have to give her an injection to quieten her down,' said Dr Stöhr.

The knocking continued. Dr Stöhr opened the door a few inches and called out angrily:

'If you don't stop that I'll have you sent to the observation ward.' And to me he said: 'We've got our own nerves to consider after all.'

The knocking became more and more insistent.

'Doctor, dear, my poor son! They've set on him and they're torturing him. They're beating him to death with sticks and stones. Help! Go down to the cellar!'

There was a sudden silence. The nurses had taken the old lady away for a bath. Long hot baths have a soothing effect.

'But why don't you try and make her see that her son isn't in the cellar?' I asked.

Dr Stöhr laughed.

'My dear young friend, she trusts what she hears going on

18

in her head more than she does me. Hallucinations convey just as strong a sensory impression as anything else. If someone tried to persuade you now that I wasn't standing in front of you talking to you, wouldn't you refuse to believe him?'

'But,' I persisted, 'if someone were to go down to the cellar with her, she would have two conflicting sensory impressions. Surely it would be possible to convince her that her son wasn't in fact being tortured down there?'

'But she's mad, don't you see? Her senses are attuned to her madness, not to reality!'

'But surely even madness has some sense of reality? When sane people experience a delusion, it's true they're able to distinguish it from reality in retrospect but at the time the reality and the delusion seem inseparable. The delusion is experienced as if it were reality. Why shouldn't the reverse be possible? Why shouldn't reality be absorbed into the delusion? Have you ever been down to the cellar with her?'

'So, on the very first day of your career as a psychiatrist you invent a new cure: the evidence of the patient's own eyes!' Dr Stöhr seemed almost angry. 'Still, I can't very well stop you taking her down to the cellar if you want to. I'll speak to the Director about it.'

The next day I went down to the cellar with the old lady. The Director was amused by his new assistant's enthusiasm but contrary to expectation he ordered that he should be given the key.

'One mustn't discourage the spirit of enquiry in the young' had been his comment.

The old lady and I crawled into every nook and cranny of the vast cellar that lay underneath the clinic. It was summer time and the heating was off. The old lady tapped the walls, looked into all the boilers, shifted some crates away from the wall and shone her torch onto the great mountains of coke. At last, she said she was satisfied.

'You're quite right, doctor dear. My son isn't here. How happy I am. It's all untrue.'

I took her back to the ward. So, my idea hadn't been so bad after all. I had dispelled a localised delusion by taking the patient to the place to which it was attached and letting her see for herself.

But I hadn't been back in the surgery long before I heard a gentle knocking at the door of the ward again:

'Doctor, dear, they've just attacked my son in the street and carried him off to the cellar. Help doctor! They're beating him up, they're doing horrible things to him. Oh, my poor son!'

Dr Stöhr looked at me quizzically but also with a certain sympathy.

'You see, madness is stronger than every form of reason. Otherwise, it wouldn't be madness.'

'Has she got a son at all?'

'Oh yes, the son's real enough.'

'Where does he live? I'll write and tell him to come and visit his mother. When she sees that he's safe and sound she can't go on thinking he's being tortured in the cellar.'

I looked up the old lady's file and dictated a letter to her son. He arrived at the clinic a few days later. The old lady wept and fell on his neck. She looked all round him, felt him all over, and finally convinced herself that she had been in the wrong. She ran across to the surgery and. called through the keyhole:

'Doctor, dear! I'm so happy. My son's alive. Alive and well.'

When it was time for her son to say good-bye to her, he said:

'Now don't worry, will you, mother dear? I'm perfectly all right. No one's going to do me any harm.'

Then he left. The old lady stayed by her bed listening. Suddenly she let out a scream, ran quickly across to the surgery door and hammered on it with her fists, crying:

'Doctor, doctor, now they've attacked my son just as he was trying to leave the clinic. They've carried him off to the cellar. They'll torture him and murder him there. Help! Help!'

She had to be taken off forcibly to the observation ward.

This time Dr Stöhr made no attempt to hide his sarcasm.

'*Your* madness, young man—this mad idea of yours that a schizophrenic delusion can be cured by confronting it with reality is fortunately curable. But the more real madness of this poor creature is beyond all cure. Don't you know the definition of a delusion?'

'A delusion is an incorrigible error of the mind originating in illness.'

'Yes, you seem to know your theory all right. But it's time you learnt to put it into practice. I admit it's not easy to say exactly what madness consists of. It's a flaw in the reasoning faculties as well as in the imagination. Its roots go very deep. It's not eliminated as easily as you thought. Well, are you cured?'

'Yes, *I* am,' I said with resignation. 'But I still can't help thinking of that poor old lady and *her* madness.'

'Now, don't start getting sentimental!' cried Dr Stöhr. 'The Director will throw you out if you show depressive tendencies. If you want to be a psychiatrist, you must learn to harden yourself to the grimmer side of life. Otherwise, you'll never be able to deal with mental illness at all.' After a while he added: 'Do you feel like having something to eat with me down at the Wild Man this evening? I've ordered snails for two. A man needs a little civilised relaxation now and again.'

We picked up our hats and left. There was no more knocking at the surgery door. But in the observation ward the old professor's wife sat among gibbering and gesticulating lunatics mumbling quietly to herself:

'Sister dear, please go down to the cellar. They've caught my poor son and are torturing him. They're beating him with sticks and stones.'

But the sister had other things to worry about. The old lady's voice grew quieter. She was exhausted. When towards midnight she started up again she was given an injection of skopolamin. Then she was quiet. The drug wrapped its dark cloak mercifully about her madness.

Chapter 2

When the meal was over, I brought the conversation back to my experience with the old lady.

'But do we know what reality is?' I asked Dr Stöhr. 'Surely for the Frau Professor the torturing of her son is as vivid as if it *were* real? Why do we think that she must be the victim of insane delusions? Where's the boundary line between insanity and mere error? Isn't all reality only the product of thought? Isn't all thought real? Aren't truth and error really just dependent on what the majority of people happen to think?'

'At first sight,' answered Dr Stöhr. 'You might say that there was no difference between an imaginary hundred mark note and a real one. But you notice the difference as soon as you start trying to buy something.'

'Substitute hell for the cellar where the boilers are—suppose the patient believes her son is being tortured down in hell. Can we still say she's mad?'

'You'd have to go down to hell with her to see for yourself!'

'Unfortunately, I don't believe in hell, so I can't even visit it in imagination.'

'Did you ever believe in it?'

'I stopped believing in it when I started thinking for myself.'

'What made you believe in hell before? Did you only believe in it because other people did?'

'I didn't dare question the beliefs of my parents and teachers.'

'And when one day you stopped believing wasn't it partly because other people had their doubts?'

'Certainly. Otherwise, the burden of proof of the nonexistence of hell would have been on me.'

'Now do you see the difference between belief, superstition and madness?'

'You mean madness contradicts what it is possible to believe? Is that it?'

'When something that it is possible to believe receives the sanction of society it's called a belief. When it doesn't it's called a superstition. One doesn't have to experience hell to be able to believe in it. But when an individual, on the basis of his own personal experience, holds something to be real which is contrary to the experience of every other individual then he is said to be mad.'

'But why don't we just say he's wrong? Why shouldn't an individual have his own individual way of being wrong? Why shouldn't I nourish a delusion as a sort of luxury? Why should it make me mad? To err is human. If there's any pattern to life, then error has its place in the pattern. Man is more adaptable than the animals, which think less and therefore make fewer mistakes. Surely the madman in his error has his place in the world?'

'Error is merely the result of wrong judgment.'

'And what about madness? Wasn't I taught for my exam that: "a delusion is an incorrigible error of the mind originating in illness"? The only thing I don't see is what the illness consists in. If I try to determine it statistically, that is to say try and measure it, the concept of illness is no use to me at all. Sane and insane are merely like interchangeable stones in a mosaic—in the mosaic of the world as we see it.'

'The sane man forms his judgment from a consciousness of reality which corresponds with the world around him. Otherwise, he wouldn't be sane. I agree that as a definition this is like a snake swallowing its own tail, but the madman has a consciousness of reality that doesn't correspond with the world around him and his error is more comprehensive, more complete, and more permanent than the sane man's. The sane man who falls into an error is capable of being right. He has the tools with which to arrive at a right judgment—he just sometimes uses them in the wrong order. When he sees his error he can correct himself. The illness in madness consists in the state of mind prior to judgment. A madman's judgment is a slave to his madness. The madness doesn't arise from wrong use of the tools, which is why reasoning is a useless tool with which to try and put him right. He makes quite different sense of his world from the sense we make of ours. The madman...'

'Complete madness, yes, I understand that. But when I went down to the cellar with the old lady and confronted her delusions with reality, why was it that her madness didn't immediately dominate what she saw? Didn't the patient in fact see the cellar as it really was? And wasn't she, for a few minutes at least, cured because her delusion seemed improbable even to herself?'

'That's because her hallucinations are merely aural ones, and capable of being temporarily blotted out by a visual impression.'

'Has madness then a choice between different forms of delusion?'

'We don't know that. Perhaps hallucinations are just thoughts which have become visible or audible.'

'So, madness distorts a person's entire consciousness and his personality with it. It completely possesses him. He's possessed in fact.'

'To suppose that devils actually enter into a man and take possession of him is a very simple and vivid way of expressing the idea of madness, but it won't do for us anymore. We're more enlightened these days. Besides a psycho-pathological approach excludes all possibility of a "personal" madness.'

'Oh, let's forget about the psycho-pathological approach. Where does that get us? Either to a new sort of madness or a confession of ignorance. Who can tell me what madness is and what it isn't? Just as we think there's something wrong with the old lady who has delusions about her son being tortured in the cellar, so she must think there's something wrong with us because we don't hear him crying out. Who's to decide who's in the right?'

'The majority, my dear fellow. Psychiatry has a democratic basis.'

'No, seriously: can you tell me exactly where the difference lies between those of us who imagine ourselves sane and those we call insane?'

'Yes,' said Dr Stöhr. 'Our moments of clarity last longer.' And with that we turned to other things.

26

Chapter 3

Dr Stöhr said:

'The Director has asked me to keep an eye on your scientific progress. Your analytical gifts lead me to suppose that you may become quite a credit to us in time. But I'm afraid you're rather too soft-hearted. What actually made you take up medicine?'

'I don't find it easy to say very definitely what made me become a doctor,' I replied. And my mind wandered back eight years or so.

I was in the Upper Fifth in the High School at R. at the time, studying on the modern side. I hadn't yet decided what I was going to be.

A friend of my parents' fell ill and was taken off to hospital. I was asked to go and visit him. He was a chemist called Schröter. It was the first time I had ever seen anyone seriously ill. I couldn't think what was the matter with him. I had known him as a man who enjoyed his life to the full and who had a certain local reputation for the excellence of his liqueurs. Now he lay there as if all the joy of living had gone out of him. He ate almost nothing, spoke in low tones and then only of dying. He didn't tell me why he wanted to die. Only once he hinted something about having sinned grievously against mankind and not wanting to go on living. I assumed that the chemist must have accidentally put too much poison in somebody's medicine and that he was dreading his punishment. So, I asked my father, who was chief magistrate in R. and thus knew about pending criminal cases, whether Schröter could expect a heavy sentence. I learnt that my supposition was 'utter nonsense'.

I was sitting by the sick chemist's bed another time when the doctor came round.

'Well, and how are we to-day?' he asked the patient. And to me he said: 'Don't move. I'll be going in a minute.'

'I think I'm a little better to-day,' said the sick man in a low voice, somehow managing a smile.

'Ah, that's it,' said the doctor. 'We mustn't lose heart. But we must try and eat our meals properly, that I do ask.'

The doctor took hold of the patient's hand, felt his pulse for a moment, looked at the chart at the end of his bed, said, 'Good evening', and walked out again.

'Do you really feel better?' I asked the chemist.

'No, as a matter of fact,' he replied.

'But why did you tell the doctor you were feeling better when you weren't?'

'Oh well, you see, every day he asks me if I'm feeling better. He's a very clever doctor, you know. I wanted to give him a little pleasure. I don't like to be his only failure. I feel so bad about not being able to make any progress.'

When I came back to see him some days later at the usual time, I found him completely changed. His face was quite lifeless, but set in an expression of fury, even though his eyes were closed. He's quite unaware of his surroundings, I said to myself. After a while he opened his eyes and looked at me in desperation.

'I can't pray any more,' he said.

'What's happened?' I asked. I felt utterly bewildered.

The sick man jerked his head slightly to one side. The movement was almost imperceptible. My eye fell on the bed-side table where a letter was lying.

'Shall I read it?' I asked.

The sick man nodded. I picked up the letter and read it. It was a note from the headmaster of the girls' school. He said that the local police had reported that Gertrude Schröter, daughter of the chemist Willi Schröter, had 'spent the night of the 6th-7th October 19—in the Hotel Hafeneck with a pupil from the boys' high school called Werner Dachsig. There could be no doubt that ...'

I read no further. A convulsive sob from the sick man made me look up. He was sitting bolt upright in bed and staring wildly about him.

'And they who have worshipped the beast,' he cried, 'shall be damned to all eternity. And they shall have no rest, either by day or by night ...'

He fell back exhausted onto the pillows.

One of the ward sisters came hurrying in at once.

'But Herr Schröter, that's no way to go on!'

She straightened his pillows, cast a dubious glance at me and hurried out again. The sick man seemed to have recovered his composure. Then the doctor came in, looking very worried.

'Now then,' he said. 'What's our trouble to-day?'

Some intuition made him reach out for the letter on the bedside table, as if the clue to the problem might lie there. But the sick man snatched it out of his hand and hid it under the blanket.

'Sister,' said the doctor in some embarrassment, and when he saw that the sister was no longer there he rang the bell and waited.

'Sister,' he said when she came in. 'Please see that the patient is spared every form of excitement.' And turning to me he said: 'No more visits for the present if you don't mind!' And then to the sister again: 'The usual dose of luminal and one or two phanodorm in addition this evening.' And to the sick man: 'Now we really must try and get a good night's sleep, Herr Schröter.' It seemed to me as if Herr Schröter didn't hear a word the doctor said. 'Tomorrow morning we'll have a really good talk about everything,' concluded the doctor.

The sister brought up an invalid table and spread a white cloth over it.

'I'm going to bring you something to eat now,' she said. 'And then you'll be able to get a really good sleep. And tomorrow morning you and the doctor will be able to have a really good talk about everything.'

As I left the room I knew that I should never see the sick chemist again.

When I got home my mother asked me how he was, but I didn't answer. I didn't trust myself to say what I felt.

The next day when I came home from school at lunchtime, I heard that Herr Schröter had died suddenly. I went to the funeral with my parents and when it was over, I asked my father why there had been no priest to walk beside the coffin. I was told that the sick man had hanged himself from the crossbar of his window during the night.

A few weeks later my father came to see me in my room.

'I've been having a word with your form master,' he said. 'You've obviously got quite a good chance of moving up next term. It's just in French and English that you're rather behind-hand.'

'I know,' I said.

'He also tells me that he's been asking you all whether you want to go on to the university. Did he ask you what you wanted to study there?'

'Yes,' I said, feeling embarrassed.

'And what did you say?'

'That I wanted to study medicine.'

'Have you quite made up your mind about that?'

'Yes.'

'And what about your music?'

I didn't answer.

'Ah well,' said my father. 'You've still got some time before you matriculate. Perhaps you'll have changed your mind again by then.'

However, I stuck to my decision, even when my form master after correcting one of my French essays, said sarcastically:

'Really, Vossmenge, you translate everything from the German much too literally. You must try and form an idea of the sentence as a whole and then translate it into an equivalent sentence in French. The German and French ways of saying a thing are entirely different. But you simply translate word for word. You stick far too close to the dictionary. What you write isn't wrong exactly, but it just isn't French. So, you want to study medicine, eh? Is it your knowledge of French grammar that you imagine is going to make you a good doctor?'

Here Dr Stöhr interrupted me.

'This is getting very confused,' he said. 'What exactly has the death of the puritanical chemist got to do with your decision to take up medicine?'

'Up to that time,' I replied, 'I had regarded doctors almost as if they were gods. When I was a child I only needed the doctor to come and stand by my bed to be cured at once. I would never have dared to think of taking up medicine so long as I held doctors in this sort of reverence. But my visits to the sick chemist had made me see that things were different from what I had imagined. The doctor treated the chemist simply as a case and not as a human being at all. So I asked myself, what was the difference between a doctor and a vet. Both set about their problems in the same sort of way. The only difference was that a doctor talked to his patients. But how did he talk to them? He said: "Now we really must try and get a good night's sleep," and "We mustn't lose heart you know". What on earth was the use of that, I asked myself. The chemist was in a state of deep depression. The doctor could see this, but he was unable to do anything about it. All he could do was to say to the sister: "See that he doesn't get over-excited." Did he think she had supernatural powers of some sort? Or did he just want to shift the responsibility onto her? Or did he simply have no idea at all of what was going on in the mind of this wretched man who despaired of his God because his daughter had gone to bed with a high school boy? At any rate *I* had an idea. And it seemed to me that all this opened up a field that was well worth exploring. I was certain of one thing and that was that one day I should at least be able to do better than that particular doctor, who could see nothing but his patient's body and had no idea what was going on in his mind.'

'And have you never regretted your decision to study medicine?' asked Dr Stöhr.

'Yes,' I said, 'I have.'

And again my thoughts went back a number of years.

Chapter 4

During my first term at the University of Freiburg I was often on the point of giving up medicine altogether. I attended the anatomy and histology lectures regularly enough, but it was the personality of the lecturer, Professor von Moellendorf, which drew me, rather than interest in the bone structure of the human body. The law lectures intrigued me most. Professor Kern really knew how to bring the criminal law to life. On the other hand, I found myself repelled by my fellow-students' careless and purely intellectual attitude to all forms of wrong-doing, which they saw solely as a matter for the apparently inflexible letter of the law. It was as if they themselves were not ordinary erring human beings but infallible calculating machines.

Professor Kern once started his analysis of a hypothetical case with the words: 'Let us suppose A kills his mother-in-law with an axe ..." He was interrupted by a wild burst of applause. I was deeply shocked. It seemed to me wrong to approve even of a hypothetical murder in this way. I began to protest indignantly. Before going on Professor Kern said: 'Well at least, gentlemen, one of you is prepared to give the proverbially wicked mother-in-law her due.'

Just before the end of the term Kern went into the subject of the reliability of eye-witnesses. While he was speaking the door suddenly burst open and a man in a light-coloured raincoat rushed towards him. Before the Professor could take cover, a shot rang out. He fell from the platform with a cry and collapsed onto the floor of the lecture hall. Most of the students simply remained paralysed in their seats. One or two jumped up and tried to catch the assassin. But he disappeared as suddenly as he had come. Some of the others then remembered the Professor who was lying groaning on the floor. All of a sudden—in fact only a few seconds had elapsed since the firing of the shot—the Professor sprang to his feet as if come to life again. He jumped up onto the platform with a laugh and called out: 'It was all a piece of acting gentlemen. I'm quite all right. But think how valuable your evidence would have been if it had been a real murder. Now I want you all to write down exactly what you saw. Describe the people involved in as much detail as possible. I'll collect your statements from you in a quarter of an hour.'

I had seen quite clearly that the 'assassin' had had nothing in his hands as he rushed at the Professor. So, it couldn't have been he who fired the shot. On the other hand, I had seen the puff of smoke from the blank cartridge. It must have been Kern himself who had fired it.

I wrote out my statement accordingly.

The next day Professor Kern could hardly disguise an impish pleasure at the amount of human error that had been revealed.

'Take a tip from me, gentlemen,' he said. 'And never believe more than ten per cent of what you see with your own eyes!'

Then he proceeded to evaluate the evidence. Only eighteen per cent of the audience had described the 'assassin' in a way which would have been of any use to the police in a hue and cry. 'Two of you gave me a bald head, gentlemen, although you've had ample opportunity to study my head of hair for forty-five minutes every day. Only one of you perceived correctly that it was not the intruder who fired the shot but myself.'

Professor Kern continued: 'Gentlemen, what you thought you saw was not what happened but what seemed to you the logical thing to have happened. For accurate observation you need a cool eye, the ability to suspend all thought- process, and the courage to stick firmly by your own opinion. You, gentlemen, on the other hand use your eyes to see what you expect to see. You allow your perceptions to be dominated by preconceived ideas. But don't worry, you're no worse than most people. The evidence of eye-witnesses is always just about as unreliable as yours was in this case. That was all I wanted to prove to you.'

Then he added: 'If there's a Herr Vossmenge here, I'd like him to come and see me during the break.'

'You're not down on my list at all?' began Professor Kern. I told him that I hadn't yet decided whether to be a doctor or a lawyer.

'So far as I can tell on the strength of a single test,' he said, 'I should say your gifts are peculiarly suited to the natural sciences. The first requirement for a lawyer is clear thinking, but the first requirement for the scientist is accurate observation. What is it you don't like about your medical studies?'

I told him my doubts about becoming a doctor arose from

the way in which anatomy and physiology were allowed to dominate psychology in medicine, or rather the way in which the anatomical and chemical aspects of life were always emphasised at the expense of the human and sociological aspects. I felt myself attracted by criminal law because in it one found man, with all his passions, in direct conflict with an arbitrary legal system imposed on him from without.

'I think I see what you mean,' said Professor Kem, 'But there's one branch of medicine in which you'll find man in conflict with a system devised by an even higher authority than the human one which prescribes the laws. Perhaps you could call it the most difficult branch of all science because in it you find man in conflict with the whole structure of the world in which he lives.'

'And what branch is that, Herr Professor?'

'Can't you guess? I mean psychiatry.'

Here Dr Stöhr interrupted me.

'So that's how you got involved in psychiatry. I get the impression that a good deal of your life has been determined by accident, or by the haphazard remarks of other people.'

'What do you mean by an accident?' I asked him.

'Now you're not going to try to get a confession of faith out of me, I hope? I'm afraid, you wouldn't like it. I think you want to go into everything too deeply. There's a surface to our mind you know, as well as depth. One can get along quite nicely on that. However, in this place you'll soon learn to grow a shell of cynicism over that soft heart of yours.'

'I don't see why I should.'

'You wait and see. But be on your guard against one thing: namely, treating your patients here not as clinical cases but as creatures of flesh and blood. That won't get you anywhere. All this modern talk about medicine being "unimaginative" because it treats human beings as if they were so many bales of goods is just a lot of nonsense. Patients have to be treated as cases. The moment we doctors start allowing ourselves feelings we lose all ability to think clearly. We're not poets; we're not concerned with people's inner lives. You got far too worked up about that schizophrenic old woman recently. You must try to stop thinking in human terms and think in terms of psychopathology or physiopathology or physico-chemistry instead. Once you're sufficiently experienced and master of your subject you can start being a human being again. A good doctor is a man who knows not only a lot, but a tremendous lot.'

'But in that case,' I replied, 'surely he should know something about human suffering too, I mean, on his own account. Only someone who knows the meaning of suffering can help to alleviate it.'

'Utterly wrong, my dear young friend,' said Dr Stöhr. 'No patient was ever cured by a doctor's sympathy. A doctor isn't on the patient's side in an illness, he's against him.'

Chapter 5

The next morning I was allowed to examine a patient on my own for the first time. She turned out to be a remarkably pretty young woman who had just arrived at the clinic. She stopped at the surgery door for a moment as she came in, looking anxiously about her. I stretched out my hand towards her and felt myself blushing. She was so young. She didn't take my hand, but stared at me out of big round eyes, trying to decide what this strange man in the white coat wanted with her. She sat down nervously. I asked her one or two simple questions. She told me her name in a low voice. When I asked her about her parents she said:

'What are they going to do to me here?'

'Nothing,' I said. 'You're ill.'

'What is this place then?'

'A hospital.'

'What's the matter?' she asked suddenly. 'Something's

happened.'

'What sort of thing?'

'I don't know, but something has happened.'

'Did you come to the clinic of your own accord?' I asked.

'Yes. I came here once before, yesterday evening, but they wouldn't let me in.'

She told me her experiences of the previous night.

After supper her husband had gone out to work on the night shift. She had put her child to bed and done the washing-up and at once had begun to feel very restless. First, she thought the child was ill. It was breathing so strangely. Later she began to think that her husband might have an accident. As she couldn't get to sleep, she went out to look for her husband. She had only gone a hundred yards or so when she began to think she had lost her way. Everything seemed different. It seemed odd to her that the birds should be singing in the parks. The blackbirds had never sung at that time of night before. Then she began to think that she was meeting the same men over and over again. In addition to which it seemed to her that some of these men were wearing false beards. Everything seemed so queer, and the trams started sending her signals.

'The trams?' I said, interrupting her. 'How do you mean, signals?'

'With their bells,' she said.

'But there's nothing remarkable about a tram ringing its bell!'

'These were ringing their bells differently. I had the feeling that they were trying to warn me of something.'

She had spent half the night wandering about the town tortured by anxiety. She hadn't dared to go home. Finally, she went to the maternity clinic and asked for the doctor who had delivered her two years previously. This doctor succeeded in calming her down and told her to go to the mental clinic and ask for Dr Stöhr. She did that. But the clinic was now closed. She rang and after some time a porter appeared. She asked if she could see Dr Stöhr.

'At this time of night?' said the porter indignantly. 'Are you mad? You can't see a doctor before nine o'clock.'

So, she spent the rest of the night wandering round and round the clinic. She must have been round it several hundred times.

Every now and again while she was telling this story she would interrupt herself and say:

'What's the matter? Something must have happened.'

Suddenly she asked me,

'Are you the examining magistrate?'

'Why should I be? Have you done something wrong?'

'I don't know. But you look so severe.'

'Examining magistrates don't usually wear white coats like doctors, do they?'

'I thought as much,' said the patient 'You're either the examining magistrate or the Public Prosecutor. You've put on a white coat so that I shouldn't realise.'

At this point the sister came in and said that the patient's husband had arrived and badly wanted to talk to his wife. The man was in a great state of excitement.

'What are you doing here?' he asked her. 'How did you get here?'

He took no notice of me at all.

'Dr Werner at the maternity clinic sent me,' she said.

'But why?' And he turned to me: 'May I ask on what authority you're keeping my wife here?'

'Your wife came to us of her own free will.'

'Is that true, Resi?'

'Ssh,' said the patient, 'or they'll never let me out again.'

'So that's it! A prisoner! Do you doctors think you can just go and lock up an innocent woman like this against her will? I'll bring a charge of unlawful detention against you.'

'But your wife's ill,' I said.

'I can well believe it. It's enough to make anyone ill—enticing a perfectly sane person into a madhouse and then locking them up in it. It would even make me ill.'

'Help me, darling,' cried the patient suddenly in desperation. 'I think I'm going mad!'

'Do you see, doctor? Do you see what you've done? Yesterday evening there was nothing wrong with my wife at all and now you've got her thinking she's mad. It's all your fault. That's all you doctors can do for people nowadays: make them ill! But you'll pay for this,' he cried. And he seized hold of the collar of my coat.

The sister now stepped in between me and my visitor. He didn't dare touch her. His rage gave way to dumb despair. He left the room.

Dr Stöhr had been watching the scene.

'You must be prepared for that sort of thing,' he said. 'Some explanation has to be found when a strapping young woman like that turns schizophrenic overnight. This reasoning process is common enough: the woman is perfectly well one day and in a mental clinic the next—therefore she is ill because she finds herself in a mental clinic among the mentally sick. It seems a rather primitive form of reasoning to us, but it serves its purpose. You'll have to get used to people blaming psychiatrists for the existence of mental illness.'

'It's easy enough for them,' I said. 'Personally, I don't know who's the madder: the husband or the wife.'

44

'I hope you haven't let the incident upset you?' asked Dr Stöhr. 'The good psychiatrist must always remain master of the situation. Yes, even when someone comes up and stabs him in the back with a carving knife.'

'I wouldn't have minded if it had been she who had insulted me,' I said. 'But the man seemed perfectly normal.'

'Normal?' asked Dr Stöhr. 'Did you say normal? Which of us is normal?'

Chapter 6

∿∿∿∿∿∿∿∿∿∿∿∿∿∿∿∿∿∿∿∿∿∿∿∿∿∿∿∿∿∿

I spent until midnight writing up the case.

'The patient is in the early stages of schizophrenia. Apart from her desperate expression, she shows no external symptoms of the disease. There is no evidence either of faulty reasoning or of hallucinations. Nor do the patient's remarks specifically indicate madness. Yet her general state of mind is obviously extremely imbalanced. She puts her own interpretation on events in the outside world. Everything seems very sinister to her. She can't say what it is that makes her so anxious but her anxiety is undoubtedly genuine. She feels that there's something in the air, something vague and indefinable, something terrifying. Terrifying just because it is vague and indefinable. One gets the impression that the patient is suffering appallingly.

'Perhaps in schizophrenia one sees man's most primitive fears working their way up from the unconscious. In prehistoric times his sense of anxiety on emerging from his cave was perfectly justified. There might indeed have been an enemy waiting for him behind every tree. And ever since those times his life has been one long search for security. Perhaps the whole course of his several hundred-thousand-year civilisation has been determined by this need for security. Only a few people have ever been able to rise above it—in former times: great commanders, conquerors, and knights of chivalry; to-day: financiers, industrialists, gamblers. The pleasure sought by such people is the pleasure of triumph over danger. Perhaps they are as courageous as they are just because unconsciously they are the most cowardly of all.

'I have a friend who takes his life in his hands rock-climbing every Sunday. Recently I told him how astonished I was at his courage.

'"If you only knew what a coward I was!" was his reply. "It's the thrill of overcoming danger that takes me up into the mountains every week-end. I have only one pleasure in life: triumph over fear. All human enterprise—in so far as it's not determined by purely animal needs—springs from this desire of man to triumph over himself. It's at the root of all culture, all religion. That's the difference between man and the animals: man can be his own master."

'Perhaps this point of view is more widely held than we realise. Certainly it's true that most of the great men of history have been abnormal. Alexander drank prodigiously all the time. During the last years of his life he was permanently drunk. In addition, he was a neurotic by psychoanalytical standards. He hated his father and loved his mother. In Kleitos he was really destroying his father figure. Julius Caesar also drank. Cato openly called him a drunkard. His epilepsy may well have been induced by his drinking bouts. Napoleon was a terror as a child and all his courtiers later went in fear of him. He was the victim of boundless ambition. Everyone was terrified of his outbursts of rage. He too had a strong mother-fixation. Paoli was the father figure he overthrew, the man whom he had once respected as a father. Fear of death and triumph over the fear of death—were these perhaps the twin driving forces in human history?

'But this patient's anxiety neurosis suggests another idea as well: thought is a simultaneous process of both perception and judgment. There is no such thing as pure perception. When I hear a tram ringing its bell I decide that it is ringing it to warn pedestrians. Or I decide that it's warning me personally. In the first case I am unaffected by unconscious fears. I exercise my judgment in the light of an experience that has hitherto proved valid, namely that trams ring their bells to warn people to get out of their way. This is the meaning I attach to the ringing of the bell the moment I hear it. But if I'm in an acute state of anxiety I put a different interpretation on it. Now it seems to me that the tram is ringing its bell to warn me of some threat to myself. Or should it be the other way round: I give the ringing of the bell a personal significance and that is why I am in a state of anxiety? Which comes first, the state of anxiety or the delusion? One thing is certain: we make some form of judgment about everything we see and that judgment is inseparable from the state of mind we are in when we make it.

'According to this then the sane man is the man who goes through life oblivious of the dangers and uncertainties by which he is beset, who attaches no personal significance to things which do not concern him, who is quite at home in the world just as he finds it. He accepts the world with a child-like trust and belief in God. The sane man is the man whose judgments are unaffected by anxiety or, to put it better, who doesn't waste time thinking about the dangers which surround him. The sane man in other words is the man who is completely insensitive to the background of his life. This complete numbness of the human senses is normality. But who can be called normal in that case? A cow in a meadow!'

The next day Dr Stöhr handed me back my diagnosis.

'This is a clinic,' he said, 'not a philosophical college. Besides, let me give you a piece of advice. Don't let yourself get involved in profound philosophical speculations while you're here. When you're writing out a diagnosis keep strictly to the facts. You can make full use of your imaginative powers later when you write your autobiography.'

'And anyway,' he added, 'you put here that a cow in a meadow can be called normal. Young man, I'm worried by your tendency to exaggerate things. Besides I'm responsible for your scientific progress. So let a man who knows something of the world tell you this: a cow in a meadow isn't normal either. The betting is it's at least suffering from tuberculosis.'

Chapter 7

I spent about an hour first thing in the morning on subcutaneous work, and for this I went over to the men's ward. I didn't leave until ten when the barbers arrived to shave the patients and cut their hair. Until then I did my best to secure peace and quiet for my consultations.

I was just sounding a consumptive when a young man came into the ward wearing a white smock with a blue collar such as the barbers wore. The interruption rather annoyed me. I went over to the door, took the intruder by the shoulders and pushed him gently but firmly out again.

'You can't start shaving here until ten o'clock,' I said.

Afterwards I learnt that this was the new Pastor who had recently been attached to the clinic for the benefit of the Protestant patients and that I had prevented him from attending to his spiritual duties. I apologised to him, though I thought it unlikely that he would ever forgive me for this first encounter.

The new Pastor's name was Kurt Degenbrück and he worked tirelessly and unceasingly for the welfare of his patients. One day he called on me to tell me that a number of patients were being kept in the clinic without any justification. In his opinion many of them had absolutely nothing wrong with them at all. I said that it wasn't easy for an amateur to decide such things; people who were mentally ill were often very clever at concealing the fact and. appeared perfectly well to outsiders.

'What you call mental,' said the Pastor, 'I prefer to call spiritual. And if the spirit is sick then it is only through the spirit that it can be healed. That is why I pray with my patients even when only a vestige of the spirit appears to remain. And I dare say that accounts for many of the recoveries which you put down to your medical skill.'

He seemed to think that I might not altogether rule this out and continued:

'Doctor, a noble and most distinguished lady is being detained in the Director's private wing, and she's the victim of a monstrous injustice. She's the wife of a well-known industrialist. However, he apparently is a man of unsurpassed meanness. His wife is a good kind woman who really has something of a saintly disposition even though she leads the life of a prisoner here. But her husband is a hard-hearted bigot who can't bear her to do good. He's undoubtedly a man with influence in high places and I'm sorry to say that one of the high places to which his influence extends is this clinic. Otherwise, the Director wouldn't be keeping a perfectly sane lady locked up in a private ward here.'

'I can't believe that anyone is detained here without good reason,' I replied.

'Oh, doctor!' continued the Pastor, with much feeling,

'Oh, what a delusion! Psychiatry is a ruthless force. It's so impersonal. No judge or lawyer dare refute the opinion of an established psychiatrist. He has the power of life and death over his patients. Or if not the power of life and death at least the power to say whether they shall be free or not. My dear doctor, everyone knows that if you want to get rid of a person you only have to go to a psychiatrist. And this is particularly true of the higher ranks of society. Doctors, lawyers and industrialists are always having those for whom they have no more use put away like this. In the old days they would simply have had them murdered. I shouldn't like,' went on the Pastor, getting more and more excited, 'to have to atone to mankind for the sins of the psychiatrists. Don't you see how arrogant you all are in your attitude towards Christ for instance, writing Him off simply as a paranoiac?'

I drew the Pastor's attention to the fact that both Adolf von Harnack and more recently Albert Schweitzer had attempted serious historical biographies of Christ.

'No, doctor, I won't have that. Either Christ was the Son of God in which case such works have the Promethean intention of bringing the Son of God down to man's own level, or else Christ was just one more sectarian thinker, in which case the Gospels are merely historical documents of doubtful authenticity and I've no more use for them. But just as you psychiatrists reduce the spirit of Christ Himself to idiotic technical jargon, so your heartless diagnoses disregard the spirit of God in the humblest of men. This lady for instance in the private wing. She's trying to follow the call of Christ and do good, and you're trying to prevent her. But I shall see that you don't.'

I couldn't help admiring the determination with which the Pastor set about his task. The noble and distinguished lady had. begged him to help her give a little pleasure to all the inmates of the clinic at Christmas.

'But don't say a word to the Director, or his henchmen,' the lady told him. 'The great man himself and all these other little doctors are completely under the influence of my husband. He's bribed the lot of them. Of course, it's really my money he's bribed them with, for I brought him a dowry worth millions. But, oh, to what purpose? So that I might languish here as if I were in prison.'

Her idea was an admirable one. She wanted to present everyone in the clinic, whether patient, sister or doctor, with a little box of oranges at Christmas-time. She asked the Pastor to take the order to the Southern Fruit Company himself. 'You see I can't write a letter from the clinic here without the Director seeing it and my husband getting to hear of it.' The Pastor promised to deal with everything at once. 'And there is just one more small thing I must ask you,' said the lady. 'Would you mind countersigning the order? You see while I'm here in the clinic I'm not allowed to get at any of my money.'

So, the trusting Pastor signed his name as a sort of guarantee. He might have had second thoughts about the value of psychiatry if he had looked at the order more closely. However, no suspicion crossed his mind and he sent the letter off to the Southern Fruit Company at once.

Some days later I was the doctor on duty and was taking a rest after lunch when the telephone rang. It was the porter on the gate.

'Doctor,' he said, 'the corridor leading to the neurology wing is piled high with crates already, where shall we put the others?'

'What sort of crates?' I asked.

'Crates of oranges.'

'Oranges? Crates of oranges? Piled high with them?'

'Come and see for yourself,' said the porter. 'And here's another lorry coming now. The whole entrance hall is full already. This isn't a mental clinic anymore, it's a fruit market.'

'I'm on my way,' I said, and hurried down to the gate.

Crate after crate full of glorious golden fruit was being carried up into the house. The wide corridors which lead to the wards were nearly all full up already. Only a narrow little passage-way had been left free. I rushed up the stairs to fetch the bursar. I rattled the door of his office. In vain. A notice on it said: 'Closed from one to three.' I ran to the telephone and dialled the Director's private number.

'I'm afraid the Director can't be disturbed just now,' said a voice.

I tried to ring one of the senior doctors. There was no reply.

Meanwhile two more lorries had come up the drive. In desperation I rushed to the gate and shut it. I spoke to the carriers through the window.

'In my capacity as a state official I forbid you to unload any more of these crates. If you don't obey I shall send for the police.'

It worked.

Thus, at the last moment I just managed to save the clinic from being swamped in oranges. Two thousand crates were already stacked in the corridors. The 'noble and most distinguished lady' had ordered, for two hundred and fifty people, two hundredweight of oranges each, making twenty-five tons altogether.

The Southern Fruit Company's bill came to my friend the Pastor. The noble lady, being a mental patient, was not responsible for her actions.

I bought four pounds of oranges off my friend and said to him:

'Don't say I didn't warn you! You'll have to readjust your ideas now. What about going into the fruit business?'

Chapter 8

It didn't seem to worry the Pastor that he should now find himself in such an unusual way the possessor of twenty-five tons of oranges and with a reputation among the doctors in the clinic for fantastically naive gullibility.

'Perhaps you'll be getting me for mental observation soon, doctor,' he said to me. 'However, I comfort myself with the thought that if Christ rode into town to-day on a donkey His enemies would immediately have Him locked up as a dangerous lunatic. They made Christ carry a cross and He didn't despair of mankind. I daresay I'll manage a few crates of oranges. Besides I won't have any difficulty in getting rid of them at cost price.'

'But what about your reputation as a spiritual adviser?'

'For me,' said the Pastor, 'it is an honour to be laughed at by the eminent psychiatrists who see in Christ only a schizoid psychopath. Were it otherwise I should begin to doubt whether I was truly following in the steps of the good Shepherd.'

'But my dear sir,' I replied, 'you were dealing with a lunatic. This distinguished lady, as you call her, is a manic depressive. She's in her manic phase at the moment, conceiving gigantic projects, imagining herself to be enormously rich and ...

'You're making a fatal mistake,' said the Pastor, interrupting me with as much self-confidence as if it were I and not he who had twenty-five tons of oranges he couldn't pay for on his hands. 'You simply can't dismiss a human being as if she were nothing but a collection of psychological terms. If someone wants to do good, as this lady whom you call a manic-depressive does, and what's more to do good in a concrete way by giving a Christmas present to everyone in the clinic, you simply can't equate that will to do good with a sick impulse. If you did, you'd have to say that all good works were a sign of sickness. And I hope you don't do that?'

'Certainly not,' I said.

'So, someone whom you call mentally ill still has an ethical side to their personality and this is unaffected by your psychiatric definition. A Christian act of self-sacrifice remains a good action even when other areas of the personality are sick. The only conclusion one can draw from this is that it isn't the whole human being who is sick, as you doctors always maintain nowadays, but only a part of him.'

'Even if you were right,' I replied, 'And it was only a part of a human being that was ever sick we would still have to lock up the whole human being when necessary, and not just a part of him.'

'Of course, but say I break my ankle: the whole of me naturally has to lie in bed and not just my injured foot, but that doesn't mean that the whole of me has to be wrapped in plaster, does it? No, only the part of me that is hurt. In the same way if someone is mentally ill and has to be shut up, he doesn't have to be cut off from the world altogether. Why does this lady who has fantasies about being rich have to be so ruthlessly cut off from the rest of life?'

'What a question for you to ask after your experience with her!'

'Ah, but you must realise where I made my mistake,' said the Pastor. 'If I had checked the order form properly, I would have noticed what an absurd amount the old lady was ordering. What's more, if only I'd enquired whether she was really as rich as she made out, I would have discovered at once that her husband wasn't a millionaire industrialist at all but a retired civil servant, and I wouldn't have let the order go through. Do you consider me mentally ill?'

'Of course not,' I said.

'Well then, will you explain to me in what way my own behaviour differed from the patient's? Didn't we both order twenty-five tons of oranges? Didn't we both think it was all right for us to do so because there was enough money in some bank or other to pay the Southern Fruit Company's bill? If you psychologists were logical and behaved fairly you'd have to lock me up as well.'

'I wish I knew what you were driving at with this extraordinary argument,' I said. 'If in fact you can't pay the Southern Fruit Company's bill then you certainly will have to be locked up.'

'My dear doctor, I want to make you see that as a scientist and a doctor you're supporting a corrupt form of society. Not a day passes without some extremely shady piece of business being transacted. You must know that. If a bank lends you a sum of money and charges you ten per cent interest

59

on it, it's just as immoral as if I were to buy oranges without being able to pay for them. The only difference is that the bank's action counts as legal whereas mine doesn't. That's one of the agreed principles of a society with which I as a Christian have very little in common. Any rich person who lives off the interest from his money without working for his living is acting immorally in my view. And this is the special system, my dear doctor, at the service of which you are prepared to place your knowledge and. skill. Just to keep this corrupt economic system functioning smoothly, you have to declare that a good human being like this patient of ours is not responsible for her actions and should be locked up.'

'You forget that it is the law which has put the patient in our care. Doesn't Christ himself say "Render unto Caesar the things that are Caesar's and unto God the things that are God's"?'

'Certainly,' answered the Pastor, 'And that's why I render everything unto God.'

'Is there nothing left over for Caesar?' I added with a laugh. 'In that case, my dear Pastor, I must admit your purchases of fruit seem to me more reasonable.'

Whereupon I bought another four pounds of oranges off him.

Chapter 9

On the evening of New Year's Day 19—, I sent a message to the Pastor to come to the male reception ward. Two uniformed police officers were there with a man in handcuffs whom they had only just brought in. An accompanying certificate stated that the poor man had suddenly been overtaken by a fit of madness in the presence of a number of witnesses and was obviously sufficiently out of his mind to be a danger to the community. But for the prudent and speedy intervention of the police the man would have killed his wife with a carving knife.

'Sometimes,' said the Pastor, 'it seems to me that even psychiatrists have a chance of doing good. For instance, if there were no mental asylum for this man to be brought to and no paragraph 51 in the legal code, he'd be taken off to gaol and tried for the attempted murder of his wife.'

'But surely,' I said, 'isn't this just an example of a corrupt society trying to get rid of a man simply because God has endowed him with a fiery temperament? Perhaps he had perfectly good grounds for wanting to murder his wife.'

'No blasphemy,' said the Pastor. 'Christ's teaching is: "He who takes the sword shall perish by the sword."'

'Take his hand-cuffs off,' I said to one of the police officers.

'Wouldn't it be better to put him in a strait-jacket?' asked the Pastor.

'Well, it's all the same to us of course,' said the police officer. 'We've carried out our orders. But a strait-jacket couldn't do him any harm. I saw him go for his wife with a carving knife myself.'

'We don't use strait-jackets anymore,' I said, 'They went out of fashion about a hundred years ago.'

Reluctantly the policeman took off the hand-cuffs.

'You can go now,' I told him and his colleague.

'Well, it's your responsibility,' they said, casting a mistrustful glance at the would-be murderer.

They saluted and went out.

'Now then tell me all about it,' I said to the man, offering him a cigarette. 'I have the impression that you're perfectly sane.'

'I'm as sane as you are,' said the man, massaging his wrists. 'And this is how I came to be taken for mad.'

And he told me the following story:

He worked in a cigarette factory and lived in a small apartment with his wife and child. Two rooms, a bedroom and kitchen on the first floor of a big tenement block. There were other families living on either side of him on the same floor. In winter the kitchen stove had to provide the heating for both rooms, that is to say for the bedroom as well. That morning, New Year's Day, it had been particularly cold, and in order to get the bedroom warm his wife had built up an enormous fire. A washing line with the child's nappies on it hung from the stove pipe to the kitchen table. A Christmas tree stood on a little table between the stove and the sofa. In front of the Christmas tree stood the pram. There was a coffee cup on the kitchen table and under this he was keeping a twenty-mark note which he had recently earned by overtime. He was going to buy himself some little extra with the money though he hadn't yet made up his mind what. He used to go and look at the money several times a day to make certain that it was still there.

His wife had taken the child to see her mother who lived just round the corner. So, he was alone listening to Richard Strauss's Legend of Joseph on the radio. Everything was wonderful. The music put him in an excellent mood. It was New Year's Day. One ought to begin the New Year with a good deed of some sort, but what good deed could he do? Outside the window three unemployed men were shovelling snow into iron carts. He knew that they were unemployed because whenever there was a fall of snow the town applied to the labour exchange for men to remove it. He had been out of work for a long time himself. He knew what it was like to have to go and sign on at the labour exchange every morning. And he thought to himself: those wretched fellows have to spend their New Year's morning shovelling snow, what about buying them a bottle of beer? He hadn't much money but at least he had a job. That meant a lot these days. It was something to be grateful for.

So, he went down and bought three bottles of beer from the pub on the comer and gave them to the three men who were shovelling snow. A bottle each. 'God bless you,' they said. They had a little conversation about the weather. 'The snow's a good thing for us,' said the unemployed men. 'At least it helps us earn a mark or two. Not much of course ...' They took hold of their two-wheeled cart and started tipping the snow out down a man-hole into the sewers. But he, the would-be murderer, went back to his apartment.

As he opened the door he saw something which made his blood run cold: the whole room was in flames. Or rather not the whole room but the curtains. The stove had become red-hot and set light to the nappies on the line. Prom there the fire had spread to the curtains. Action was needed. His first instinct was to leap to the kitchen table and put his much treasured, twenty mark note away safely. He stuffed it into his overcoat pocket without thinking. Then he tore off the overcoat to give himself freedom of movement, and threw it into the bedroom, the door of which was still open. Then he slammed the door shut to prevent the fire spreading to the bed. Then with one grab he swept aside the Christmas tree which was just about to catch fire. The pram upset. He didn't hear any of the noise. He took the carving knife from the cupboard and cut the line on which the burning nap-pies were hanging. Then with one grab be brought down the blazing curtains. As they lay burning on the floor he tried to stamp them out with his hob-nailed boots. It was difficult to do this without getting burnt himself, but in the end he suc-ceeded. Soon the fire was out. He wrenched open the win-dow to let out the smoke.

The neighbours had heard the frightful noise coming from his room and had gathered in the corridor.

'What is it?' they called, as they came running up. They looked through the key-hole. They saw the Christmas tree and the pram upset on the floor and the man dancing up and down in a frenzy in the middle of the room. He

64

had a carving knife in his hand.

'He's gone mad,' they shouted, and called for the police.

The tenants of the ground floor flat were alarmed by the din overhead and came running up too.

'Someone's gone mad,' they heard people shouting on the first floor. 'Fetch the police.'

Someone ran for the police; someone else went to tell the man's wife who was with her mother round the comer. She came running round at once.

'Richard! Richard! What is it? Oh God, he's gone mad!' she cried as she opened the door of the apartment. The kitchen was in a terrible state. The Christmas tree lay on the floor, the glass decorations shattered into a thousand pieces. The pram had been overturned; the curtains torn down; it was a scene of utter chaos. And in the middle of it stood her husband waving a carving knife about in a state of great excitement. There was no longer any sign of the fire. The windows were wide open. And he was fuming with rage.

If he hadn't acted like lightning the whole house would have caught fire. And why? Because his wife had made up the fire as if she were stoking an inferno. As so often before, the man had just instinctively looked to see if the money was still there. He found that the twenty-mark note had gone from under the coffee cup. In his excitement he had forgotten that he had put it into his overcoat pocket to save it from being burnt.

'Where's the money gone?' he shrieked at his wife.

'Richard! Richard! You must be mad!' she cried.

'It's all your fault! Where's the money! It's vanished, you bitch,' he yelled, rushing at her.

And the neighbours who had been watching the scene through the open doorway cried:

'He's killing her!'

For he was still holding the carving knife with which he had cut the line.

It was at this moment that a policeman arrived on the scene. He heard the women screaming, heard someone shout: 'He's killing her', saw the excited man standing in front of his wife with a carving knife in his hand, saw the Christmas tree on the floor, the overturned pram, the torn down curtains and the general scene of chaos, and it was enough for him. With one bound he leapt into the room and grabbed the man's right wrist. The knife fell to the floor. He forced the man's arm up, slipped under his shoulder, twisted the arm behind his back and with his other hand seized him by the hair. The man could do nothing. The police had arrived in the nick of time.

The man was taken off to the police station. Hardly had the policeman let go of him when he started raving again:

'What do you want with me? It's my wife's fault. But for me the whole house would have caught fire.'

They had to put hand-cuffs on him. A Red Cross ambulance was rung up and he was taken off to police headquarters. There a certificate was made out, and the man was sent off to the mental clinic.

I listened to the story in silence. Then I rang up the district medical officer and he made out a form so that the would-be murderer could be released the same day. His wife had arrived in the meantime and had had the misunderstanding explained to her.

'Perhaps you can see from that,' I said to the Pastor, 'that it isn't psychiatrists who are ruthless, but a man's neighbours. Take a man's neighbours in the mass and you'll find them an insensitive egotistical lot, quite incapable of understanding anything outside their own experience. On the odd occasions when a sane man is brought to a mental hospital it's none of the psychiatrist's doing. Now just think how these same neighbours would behave if a genuinely sick person were to fall into their hands. No, Pastor, it isn't to rob our patients of the advantages of freedom that we shut them away, but to protect them from the outside world at whose mercy they would otherwise be. There's nothing more dangerous for our patients than what you call the freedom of the outside world.'

This seemed to impress the Pastor. He said nothing.

Chapter 10

∧∧

Dear Doctor,

Scientific authority has triumphed over religious zeal. It's a week now since I came here to devote myself to the cares of the petty bourgeois community of this little Franconian town. I've been transferred here because I 'intervened in matters which were exclusively the concern of the clinic' and 'did not have proper regard for the dignity of the Church.'

But don't think you've convinced me that I acted absurdly. You still haven't yet answered my question: how can the spirit be said to become ill? For even you whom I regard as the prototype of the intellectual sceptic, you who act not because love has made you strong but because pity has made you weak, even you cannot deny that the spirit of man is of divine origin.

You call yourself a psychiatrist. But what do you know of the soul? The Greeks called this thing which has given you your professional label: *psyche* or *anemos*. *Anemos* means breath or wind. The thought of the ancients was very vivid and unabstract and they wanted to express that there was something in man which was both intangible and beyond the grasp of reason—like the wind. And so, dear Wind Doctor, try and define the soul for me—this 'adjunct to the body', as your prophet Nietszche is honest enough to describe it.

Is psychology really a science based on well-established principles like mathematics or physics? Or is it the equivalent for our own time of what Novalis called: 'One of those masks hung in the temple in place of the true image of God'?

Has the healing force of psychology, which is what psychiatry represents, been as successful as Christ's healing with His eternal truth about the immortality of the soul?

One of the few articles of your modern philosophical or metaphysical creed I have any enthusiasm for is Emerson's sentence: 'When the soul breathes through a man's intellect it is genius; when it breathes through his will it is virtue; when it flows through his affection it is love.'

There are certain self-evident things which defeat even your rational approach. For instance, it seems to you self-evident that the mind can be sick.

But take love, which Emerson says is another aspect of the soul, like intellect. Would you also say that love can be sick? Or virtue? Anyone can be sick with love. There's no love without suffering, as the saying goes. But doesn't such suffering contain the germ of all man's nobler aspirations? Can there be any comparison between the suffering of the soul and ordinary physical infirmity? Your view of sickness is of a sort of sabotage carried out on a highly complicated machine. You remove the sand from the engine and set the points and signals at 'Go'. That's all very well if it's just a question of broken bones or an inflamed appendix. But when you talk about the mind or soul being sick you're just groping around in the dark. You don't know what the sold is when it's well, and yet you claim to be able to cure it. You want to free the world from suffering, and in a sociological sense you do reduce the risks. But you also make life less exciting. When you've achieved your goal and rid the whole world of passion and suffering, you'll find you've got a terrible new disease on your hands: boredom. This is a disease brought into being by the doctor himself. The healing which you and your colleagues try to give mankind, my dear doctor, is of human origin and can therefore be of only relative value.

How is the 'noble lady' who wanted to do good and merely erred in over-estimating her capacity to do so? And the 'would-be murderer'? Or don't you keep in touch with your flock?

Best wishes,

D.

Dear Orange Pastor,

In our search after truth we can never hope to cover the whole vast ocean of the unknown; we must always go on searching. In the same way we doctors have to go on striving towards a cure, even though a cure in the absolute sense must always evade us. Doctors aren't concerned with the absolute; we gladly leave that to priests like you. We approach problems from the practical point of view. They seem quite different from there.

I'm a great admirer of Emerson's but the sentence which you quote in your letter is no more than a pretty phrase. He substitutes three partial images for one whole one. This sort of philosophic aestheticism is useless to the natural scientist. I find another epigram of Emerson's more impressive—the one which runs: 'of immortality, the soul when well-employed is incurious.'

Emerson was undoubtedly thinking of the *sophrosyne* of the Greeks and their ability to steer a middle course between hedonism and asceticism. In order to triumph over the world

'Why?' I asked in my innocence. 'How would you define the normal man?'

'The normal man,' answered Dr Stöhr, 'is a harmless imbecile.'

With best wishes,

Yours,

V.

Chapter 11

Paul had spent the best years of his life shut up in the refractory block. In all this time no-one had ever noticed anything peculiar about him: not a trace of mental disease, not even a suggestion of prison neurosis. Paul was always quiet and friendly. He presented a permanent challenge to the skill of every new doctor who came to the block. Hitherto no one had succeeded in diagnosing his trouble. There was only one question that one wasn't allowed to ask, and that was why he had ever been sent to the asylum in the first place.

As most newcomers soon discovered after talking to Paul the only remarkable thing about him was the resignation with which he accepted his apparently unwarranted detention.

At the time of my first visit to him he was twenty-seven years old, and it struck me at once that he seemed quite unaware of his imprisonment. The conversation was very one-sided. No sooner had he discerned my interest in music than he began to talk to me about his own musical studies. A piano had been put in his room, and he had taught himself to play it. Although I protested, he made me sit down and play something for him. I chose a piece by Reger because it was one which I thought I would have no difficulty in getting through. But I never got to the end of it. Paul pushed my arm away from the keys, forced me off the piano stool and played it as he thought it should be played. It was as if I were hearing it for the first time. I left the room after a delightful piano lesson that had lasted an hour.

That evening in the common room I told my colleagues about my visit to Paul.

'Well,' they said. 'And what did you do with him?'

'Nothing,' I answered. 'He gave me a piano lesson.'

'You're lucky,' said Dr Berger, 'I went to see him every day for a year, and he taught me Persian.'

'It's very strange,' I said. 'He's held here under a judicial warrant made out ten years ago, but surely not with the object of teaching the doctors Persian? There doesn't seem to be any case history on him.'

'The Director's got it,' said the Senior Doctor. 'For a long time now he's been trying to convince the Public Prosecutor's office that Paul is completely normal. Report after report has gone onto the files there. It's just so much wastepaper, "Proposal for release dismissed." Every time the Director says that the diagnosis of schizophrenia on which Paul was committed here ten years ago was incorrect, the Public Prosecutor answers that that may well be, but that there was no mistake about the way in which Paul murdered his brother ten years ago. The Public Prosecutor doesn't care whether he's shut up in prison or a mental home, but he's got to be shut up somewhere.'

The next day the Director gave me the papers and that night I read the story of a young man who murdered his brother.

Paul came from a family which was remarkable for its musical talents. His uncle was the famous conductor N. His father taught at the musical high school in M. and had published some works of chamber music. Paul and his younger brother Herbert were also both very musical, but their father didn't want them to take up music. Neither of them was allowed a musical instrument, though they could go to concerts. Both adored music, Paul classical and Herbert modern, particularly Hindemith and jazz. Paul suffered severely from his father's ban on all forms of playing. His father was also particularly fond of classical music, but he never discussed it with Paul. Paul had never been able to make contact with his father. The old man laid down certain rules, allowed this, forbade that and in general showed little interest in his sons. Herbert was like his mother, always gay and full of life. He was very popular, had a lot of friends, and found no difficulty in showing his feelings for them. Paul was devoted to his brother but could never tell him so. His mother meant a lot to him, too, but he couldn't show his affection for her either.

The parents were often away, and the children were then able to do as they liked. The maid obeyed the orders given her by the two young sons of the house unquestioningly. On the 22nd of October 19—, Paul was woken at seven o'clock so that he should be in time for school. Paul was in the Lower Sixth at the time. Herbert, who went to the same school and was in the Lower Fifth, was allowed to stay in bed on this particular morning because he had a stiff neck. No one was ever really able to discover what happened afterwards that morning.

At about noon the maid found Herbert lying in bed with a bullet wound in the head. He was dead. It was clear that he had been shot in his sleep. The maid fetched a police-man from the street, and he sent for the detectives. At first it was supposed that someone had broken into the house for money, knowing that the mother and father were away and assuming that the children would be at school. The theory was that the intruder had been disturbed by Herbert and had shot him as the sole witness.

This theory turned practically to certainty when it was discovered that the music professor's desk had been broken open. But when Paul, whom the detectives were waiting to interview, didn't come home, a new theory was developed. A search was made for Paul, and it was discovered that he hadn't been to school at all. Within a few hours the police had discovered that at ten o'clock that morning Paul had bought himself a second-class ticket to Hamburg. The alarm was sent out to the railway police all over Germany the same evening. But Paul hadn't gone to Hamburg. He had stayed in the town, and when evening came and the police had given up look-ing for him in it he went to a night club and quietly drunk a bottle of wine. The only thing that struck the waiter was that he made disparaging remarks about the band and kept on demanding classical music. Later a girl called Anni had sat down at his table. They had left together about midnight.

Anni was interrogated and said that Paul had behaved very strangely. He had kept on smiling as if his mind was somewhere else. He had gone home with her, given her money, far more than she had expected, but hadn't touched her. He had simply lain down and gone to sleep at once. They had had breakfast together the next morning. He had seemed very cheerful. But when she had tried to find out more about him, where he came from and what he did, he had answered evasively. Then she had opened her morning paper and to her horror seen his photograph and a statement to the effect that he had murdered his brother. On the pretext of having to go out for something she went straight off and told the police.

The police collected Paul from Anni's apartment. He didn't seem at all put out by their arrival and smiled as he was led away. When he was interrogated, he admitted his crime at once.

'Yes,' he said, 'I shot my brother while he was asleep.'

He smiled absent-mindedly.

The only strange thing was that there wasn't any motive. The police put their best men on to try and find out why he had done it. You can't have a murder without a motive. But they couldn't get anything out of him. He gave the same answer over and over again:

'I just wanted to see what it felt like to murder one's brother.'

But he wouldn't go into any details about what it felt like.

The Public Prosecutor ordered him to be kept under observation in a mental clinic for six weeks. Paul gave the doctors the same answer as he had given the police. Later he simply ignored all questions. He just sat there smiling to himself. After a few weeks a sudden change took place in his behaviour. He cheered up, seemed keen to be interrogated, asked after his parents and demanded to be released. When people said to him: 'But you shot your brother', he was struck dumb as if it was the first he had heard of it. But he made no attempt to deny the fact. Each time he was asked why he had done it he simply answered: 'I don't know.' He wouldn't discuss any details of the day of the murder but was most co-operative about answering every other question.

In February 19—, a charge of murder was preferred against

him. The proceedings only lasted a day. The whole town was in a great state of excitement. People expected a sensation of some sort, but there was none. Paul said he couldn't remember anything about the murder of his brother. He smiled amiably, as he said this. When he saw his parents again he smiled at them in embarrassment.

Then a certain Professor B. gave his professional opinion. He said that as he could find absolutely no motive for the murder he could only put it down to hebephrenia, the early stage of schizophrenia. He was unable to state categorically that Paul had been suffering from the disease on the day of the murder, but his behaviour afterwards led him to suppose that this was so: particularly the vacant smile which had so struck everyone including the girl called Anni, and the fact that he was now unable to remember anything about the crime at all.

The Public Prosecutor gave the impression that he didn't intend to dispute the famous professor's opinion. Then he suddenly applied for the suspension of the trial. The murder charge was dropped and the accused was sent to a mental hospital for an indeterminate period as a danger to the community.

The diagnosis of schizophrenia had been open to question from the very first day Paul entered the asylum. After he had been there a year, the Director put in his first report to the effect that Paul was no longer suffering from any form of mental illness. The Public Prosecutor's office wrote back to say that from the point of view of re-trying the case Paul's present mental state was irrelevant. What mattered was whether he had been mentally ill when he committed, the murder. The Director couldn't give a definite answer to that. So, Paul stayed in the asylum for ten years. The Director let him have a piano in his room and all the music he wanted. Although he had never had a teacher Paul trained himself to be a first-class pianist. The Director let him have everything he wanted in the way of books. Paul learnt to write and speak four Arabic languages fluently. The Director and Paul even became close friends. They often discussed difficult philosophical problems. There was only one thing they never spoke about: the murder. When asked about it, Paul would not answer. And the Director even became quite angry when anyone brought the subject up.

'The Director wants to forget that it ever happened,' the doctors under him would say. 'If he goes on working on the Public Prosecutor much longer, he'll have him thinking that it was simply a hallucination too.'

'If someone could only lose the papers, then they'd all be able to think they dreamt it. But you can't ignore what's down in black and white.'

These were the sort of things his colleagues said. After twelve years the Public Prosecutor decided that Paul had expiated his crime. The judicial warrant of 19— was cancelled. Paul was released. He went abroad. We heard no more of him except that he gave a large number of concerts and travelled a great deal. Meanwhile I had made considerable progress with the piano myself, thanks to what I had learnt from him.

When later I came to study the works of Sigmund Freud and C. G. Jung more closely, I thought more about Paul and decided that he could hardly have been a case of schizophrenia. He would almost certainly have responded to deep analysis. But if Professor B. hadn't diagnosed Paul as schizophrenic, he would unquestionably have been sent to prison. So that at least there was something to be said for the wrong

79

diagnosis. But looked at from another point of view it was a pity that the orthodox psychiatrists of those days attached so little importance to psycho-analysis. I already knew something of the works of Freud, Adler and Jung, but as a junior doctor in a mental clinic it was my duty to forget it.

Chapter 12

Robert clearly enjoyed both the correspondence and the numerous conversations he must have had with the Pastor on the subject of this man Paul who murdered his brother. We have one of the priest's letters on the subject which runs as follows:

Dear Wind Doctor,

I found your Cain and Abel story deeply disturbing. To what horrors of loneliness had this father condemned his unhappy son Paul! What depths of melancholy that set smile of his conveys! It struck everyone, even the harlot Anni, as the smile of a man whose mind was somewhere else. Where can his mind have been? This murder of his brother seems to me like the suicide of someone who remains conscious while doing the deed. I admit I don't see this matter as a psychiatrist would, but I'm not sure I don't see more deeply into it. Paul is the suicide whose weariness with life springs from his inability, in spite of a deeply affectionate nature, to break through the barrier which separates all of us from our brothers. His murder of his brother was an attempt to break through this barrier. What a terrible curse the old music professor laid upon himself by not being able to teach his son how to communicate with his fellow men.

It so happens that I met this professor some years ago. I knew nothing of his family misfortune. He seemed to live entirely in his music. It seems to me there's a grave danger in letting oneself get too much wrapped up in music. I'm sure it can prove a most soothing and beneficial escape from the world. But one must remember that on one's return from the dream world life has to be taken up again from exactly where one left off. This is particularly true of romantic music. Music can't solve our everyday problems for us. All it can do is to reduce the tension inside us. It may perhaps make it easier for us to acquire insight into things, but it can't give us that insight unless we are prepared to make an effort of our own. I'm afraid it was because he was so buried in the dream-world of his music that the professor couldn't see his duties towards his children. I think I have come to see that all that music can do for us is occasionally to give the mind the illusion of happiness.

The lot of the unhappy Paul reminds me of Soren Kirkegaard's. He too inherited his melancholy from his father, who had turned his back on God in his youth. Kirkegaard, too, was condemned to loneliness by his father. He liberated himself from its deadly suffocating effects by treating his unhappiness creatively. Desperation drove him to his own form of religious philosophy. Our poor friend Paul liberated himself by a murder.

How extraordinary of you psychiatrists not to have realised

that the murder of his brother had made Paul all right again! For ten years you kept him under observation and still knew nothing about him! However, the loving care you showed for him redeems you. Perhaps your Director, who wouldn't accept that there was anything the matter with Paul, sensed, something of the family background to the terrible event. Still, any good you did to Paul proceeded from your humanity rather than your psychiatric skill. Psychiatry doesn't come well enough out of the story for my doubts about it to be removed.

And the detachment with which you described the case! All the very best from
Your
Orange Pastor

The following letter of Robert Vossmenge's which is undated and of which I found a copy is presumably the answer to the above letter of Pastor Degenbrück's.

Dear Orange Pastor,

Psychiatry must necessarily be useless when there is nothing wrong with the person with whom it is asked to deal. Psychiatry is always being regarded as a branch of psychology. Quite wrongly. Psychiatry only begins where psychology leaves off. A man who has nothing wrong with him—that is, if there is such a man—can understand another man who has nothing wrong with him without any psychiatric knowledge, and probably preferably without any psychological knowledge either. By psychology, I mean here not a general understanding of human nature, but psychology as a specialised science.

(N.B. Professor B. always used to say: 'There's an ordinary everyday psychology, which can be learnt from going around among one's fellow-men, and a scientific psychology which can be learnt from books and tested by experiments. Only the ordinary everyday sort is any use.')

If you confront a psychiatrist with a man who has nothing the matter with him, he's like a fireman without a fire; there's nothing for him to do. But as there is no such thing as a man with nothing the matter with him, a psychiatrist will in fact always find something to do.

My dear Orange Pastor, it doubtless does you credit that you have been so deeply affected by this case. But we have always been taught that emotion is no substitute for judgment. Only by tempering emotion with detachment can one hope to arrive at a valid judgment. When therefore you reproach me for my detachment, you must know that I adopt this as a protection. Science always demands a cool head. But psychiatry demands an ice-cold one. Otherwise, one gets nowhere with it. A doctor who allows himself to feel sorry for his patients is just spoiling his efficiency as a doctor. His feelings may do him credit as a human being, but they can do the patient no good at all.

Yours ever,

Wind Doctor

Chapter 13

Dear Orange Pastor,

I've now started holding consultations at police head-quarters at which I dispense a sort of sociological first aid. The other day a careworn and embittered old woman came to me to complain about her life. As a young girl she had been rash enough to marry a man who had taken to drink immediately after the wedding. She had been brought up in a very religious atmosphere and was determined to cure him of drink by prayer. The more he drank the more she prayed. Finally, he was drinking so heavily that she was praying all the time.

You know how drink can become a craving in the end. The depressions which go with each hang-over become so appalling that the only way of getting over them is by another bout of drinking. It's a vicious circle which eventually reduces the drinker to a wreck. Nothing is left of the various qualities he once possessed but a desire for drink and women. And as the happiness given by the bottle is a purely illusory one, his desire for women vanishes in drink as well. Rage seizes him when he can't get a drink—it's the only emotion he's still capable of. He beats his wife, turns the children out of their beds in the middle of the night and throws them out into the streets in all weathers. He breaks up the furniture, thus destroying the last remnants of a home that was once built on love and hope. In short, he drags his family down with him into his misery.

The woman who came to see me was black and blue all over. She begged me to help her, saying that if I didn't, she was lost. The man's behaviour had reached such a pitch that the children had had to be sent away. The next time her husband came home drunk, he would kill her with the chopper.

The man wasn't given a chance to get drunk again. We have extensive powers to act in cases of drunkenness and it wasn't even necessary to prove the woman's allegations. We simply made out a certificate for the police and they brought him up to us at the clinic. We put him in the refractory block. He stormed and raged there for two days, presumably because he couldn't get anything but water to drink. To-day he is suddenly quite docile. He implores us to let him go and blames his wife for driving him to drink by her perpetual nagging. He had simply had no peace at home at all.

Up to this point, my dear Orange Pastor, the case looks straightforward enough. We get something like this almost every day. It's because of the behaviour of the wife that I give you the case in detail. For years she's been praying to God to cure her husband of drunkenness. And now that He has given him to us to be cured, she prays to Him every day to let her have him back again.

Let me explain. The drunk put up a fierce resistance

when the police arrested him, and they had to hold him in a rather painful grip when they brought him in. Although it was on the wife's information that they were acting, she rushed forward and bit one of them in protest. No sooner had the man been handed over to us at the clinic than she was on her knees in front of me begging for his release. She knelt on exactly the same spot where a few days before she had begged me to lock him up before he murdered her.

What are we to make of all this? Did the wife pray because her husband drank so much, or did he drink because she prayed so much? Or was it that she simply had to have something to pray about?

With very best wishes,

Your

Wind Doctor

Dear Wind Doctor,

I can see from your question about the possibility of a man taking to drink because his wife spends too much time in Church praying, that you yourself haven't done any praying since you decided to become a psychiatrist. Of course, I know that you expect me, as a man who spends a good deal of his time praying professionally, to take the side of the drunkard's wife. Nothing doing, I'm afraid. I can't answer your question about which came first, the drinking or the praying, because I'm not a psychiatrist but only a priest. Such psychological hair-splitting is of no interest to me at all. I see you don't actually say that the woman's prayers were completely ineffectual in curing her husband of drunkenness, but only, I suspect, because you don't want to hurt me.

My dear Wind Doctor, you don't have to take my feelings into account. You can say anything you like to me. I'll even give you an answer, too, and it goes like this: you're quite wrong, God did turn the man from drink when He put him into your hands. You may say He took his time about it. Well, perhaps God has His reasons for that. For instance, I pray to God to cure you of seeing the world solely from the standpoint of a psychiatrist. Your thoughts simply go round and round in circles because you're stuck in a psychological groove. But am I to grow impatient with God and reproach Him just because so far he hasn't listened to me?

If you could have your way with theology the first thing you'd probably do would be to start a statistical investigation into the frequency with which men's prayers are answered. After that you'd try and find out the average length of time God took to answer them. If you did this honestly—scientifically, you'd call it—you'd discover what we theologians have known all the time, namely that the mind of God is beyond understanding. Which is also the answer to your question about the relationship between the wife's prayers and her husband's drunkenness—in so far, that is, as you can't find a purely psychological explanation. And that's your affair.

I found it a painful story. But I derived some comfort from the fact that the wife's only pleasure after the breakdown of her marriage lay in prayer, regardless of what she was praying for. It still seems to me better to do nothing but pray than to do nothing but drink. I even imagine that the woman would long ago have killed her drunken husband had she not daily found in prayer the strength to go on living with him.

With best wishes,

Your

Pastor D.

Dear Orange Pastor,

Two things strike me about your answer which in other respects I find not unskillful. First, you regard prayer as beneficial only to the person praying. I thought the wife's prayers were supposed to be of some use to her husband, too. He needed help more than she did. Secondly, I'm deeply touched by what you say about God sending the drunkard to our clinic to be cured—with the assistance, that is, of the morality police. Unfortunately, I must confess that He sent him too late. Even if we do eventually succeed in curing him, I'm afraid his character will have suffered irreparable damage. If you say that we doctors and nurses should have concerned ourselves with him sooner, then you're absolutely right. Unfortunately, his wife kept him from us too long. But doesn't it conflict with your professional viewpoint to suggest, as you thus do, that God acted too late in this matter?

Meanwhile I'm delighted to know that you think that God is prepared to recognise our work. Otherwise presumably you wouldn't have said that He sent the drunk to us to be cured. I remember that you once described psychiatry as 'a ruthless impersonal force'. I always thought you regarded it as the work of the devil.

With very best wishes,

Your

Robert V.

Dear Doctor,

What a very narrow view you still take of everything! You can't have thought about the nature of God very much. Otherwise, you wouldn't try and associate yourself with Him and persuade me that your counsel and His were in any way comparable. I don't know what God has in mind either for you or for the drunk, but it wouldn't surprise me if He were prepared to renounce both the drunk and his devout wife for the sake of getting you to think about Him a little. Certainly, you're in just as much, if not greater, danger than the drunk. He's finished in any case. You are steeped in pride. Perhaps God wishes to warn you, to spare you a similar plunge into misery. He may have something in mind for you in the future. And for all our sakes I hope that when the moment comes in which He needs you, you'll be able to recognise it.

Besides I never said that psychiatry was the work of the devil. Why should I bring the devil into it? Psychiatry is the work of men who sometimes have very little idea of what they are doing. It is the work of men who worship the idol of scientific authority. Perhaps there isn't all that difference between your notion of the work of the devil and my notion of the work of modern psychiatry. But while I'm always ready to dispute the basic principles of your science I don't feel I have to marshal the full force of my religious faith against psychiatry in the same way as I ask God to give me strength to do each day against the devil. So far, I've only been able to judge psychiatry by its surface manifestations, I don't know much about it. Its sociological activities are what I feel I have to criticise, particularly when they come into conflict with religion, but then only in the concrete cases which we can discuss together.

Yours,

Pastor D.

P.S. Your last letter was very cynical. If I go on writing to you, it's because you seem to me to have been misled. Misled by high school teachers with their ideas of the absolute value of science. There is only one Absolute and that is God. Everything else is superstition. Science is based not on God

but on an arbitrary set of absolutes which in fact have no more than relative value. And since Science is to-day regarded as omnipotent, you can see why I mistrust it so much. You're too young yet to be able to reject what you were taught at school. But I'm convinced that it is your faith in the authority of science which prevents you from having faith in God.
D.

My dear Pastor,

So, modern medicine is simply a form of superstition. But modern medicine has developed the diphtheria serum, for instance. Now be honest with me: if a child of yours got diphtheria, which I pray it never will—even though you will say that I know nothing about prayer—what would you do: go to a doctor, misled as he is by his worship of scientific authority and have the child inoculated, or pray for its recovery? Which would you do? Come on, now—answer me!
Yours,
Vossmenge

The answer came by telegram. It ran:
'You ass stop I'd do both
Degenbrück'

Chapter 14

I have always been puzzled why men should once have thought of epilepsy as a sacred illness of some sort. Now I think I know the answer.

This is what happened to me one night:

It must have been about two in the morning when the telephone woke me. It was the sergeant on duty who said that they had picked up a drunk on the street. He was almost unconscious and they were just taking him into my consulting room for me to have a look at. I quickly got dressed and as I stepped out into the hall, I saw two policemen at the other end carrying a man towards me. They had put one of his arms round each of their necks and had crossed their hands to form a sort of chair for him. They dumped him down in the consulting room. The man fell heavily onto the sofa and lay there motionless. His eyes were shut. He didn't react when I spoke to him.

The two policemen wiped the sweat from their brows. The man must have been over six feet tall and was built like a heavy-weight boxer. I learnt later that he was a butcher's apprentice and one of the strongest men in the trade. One of the policemen stayed behind to guard him and settling himself over in the corner away from the glare of the lamp, fell asleep on his feet. The other went down to the orderly room.

I tested the drunk man's heart and circulation and rather to my surprise found that he was in no danger of a heart attack. I then went over to the cupboard to fetch the necessary instruments with which to test his reflexes. I thus had my back to the scene when a terrible cry suddenly rang out behind me. I spun round and saw that the 'drunk' was now standing in the middle of the room. He was a terrifying sight. His eyes were wide open, and he stared about him with a quite indescribable expression. For a second, I was reminded of a picture I had once seen of a gorilla rearing up to crush its enemy in its arms. I shouldn't have been surprised to see the man pounding his chest with his fists. He did in fact raise his arms but only to hurl himself with another terrible cry straight at the policeman who had begun to stir but still had no idea of the danger he was in. It all happened in a fraction of a second. Before I had had time to realise that we were dealing not with a drunk but with an epileptic, the man had leapt on the policeman like a panther. I saw a knife flash in his hand. I knew now that both our lives were at stake. An epileptic in a fit is the most dangerous lunatic of all, indeed he is the only lunatic a psychiatrist has any reason to fear. So, it was desperation rather than courage which made me hurl myself into the fray. I caught the raving man's right wrist just as he was about to plunge his knife into the policeman, who was still paralysed with fright. Epileptics often imagine themselves beset by devils in their fits, and they are ready to sell their lives dearly. The most appalling fear of death lends them strength, a fear so appalling that we can have little idea of it. But luckily for me the man was confused by having two opponents. If he had turned on me at once as I grabbed his wrist, I shouldn't have had a chance. But he went on attacking the policeman with his left arm, and I managed to slip under his right and twist it behind his back still holding onto his wrist with both hands. If only I could have held this arm behind his back with one hand, I could have got my other hand up over his head and into his eyes and rendered him harmless. But it was impossible. The man was as strong as an ox. I could never have held him with one hand.

In the meantime, the policeman had dodged out of the comer and was trying to get away from the giant's grasp altogether. I'll take him from you,' he shouted, but it was easier said than done. I could feel my strength beginning to go. The policeman was now bleeding in several places. Whichever way he tried to turn the epileptic somehow always managed to face him. The struggle took us several times round the room, with the epileptic carrying me on his back as if I were no more than a sack. But I kept a firm grip on his arm and found myself with the knife within only a few inches from my nose.

I don't know how long the fight went on for. The only thought in my mind as the raving man carried me round and round the room was at all costs not to let go. Eventually he caught the pocket of his jacket on the comer of my desk and though it only held him up for a moment it was long enough for the policeman to be able to slip from his grasp and get round behind him. In a flash he had taken the man from me although he was still clutching the knife. I rushed to the telephone and called the orderly room for help. A moment later I heard the clatter of hob-nailed boots on the staircase. It seemed the sweetest music I had ever heard in my life, for the issue of the struggle was still in doubt. While I was at the telephone the two combatants fell heavily against my instrument cupboard and sent it crashing to the floor. This seemed to be the signal for the end of the fight. The epileptic collapsed on the floor with a gurgling sound and lay there motionless. My comrade opened the door to direct his colleagues to the scene of action, but they were no longer needed. It had been touch and go.

The next morning the Chief of Police came round in person to watch the cleaners sweeping up the debris in my consulting room. He asked me if I thought anything could have been done to prevent the incident. It was then that I realised where I had made my mistake. While examining the 'drunk' for symptoms of a heart attack I had noticed that there was no smell of alcohol about him but failed to draw the obvious conclusions.

In dangerous situations one should make use of all the senses and not just rely on the intellect. Logic is a desk weapon. It is of little value in primitive surroundings unless ordinary sensory perceptions are allowed priority over it. In our consulting room the epileptic had imagined himself back in the primaeval forest. He took us back a hundred thousand years into a world peopled with devils. That is what gives epilepsy its sacred character: it contains within it the entire span of man's existence. The epileptic was not just behaving like primitive man, he *was* primitive man and he recognised in its the devils of primitive times. And what has man become to-day? A domesticated creature with business interests, quite incapable of holding his own against devils. The idea of god and devil in a single form seems intolerable to him.

This is the sort of comment I would have made on the incident if I hadn't learnt at school to regard epilepsy solely from the standpoint of the anatomy of the brain. Meanwhile I'm grateful to my teachers for having taught me to think in terms of anatomy and pathology. The moment one starts thinking in terms of metaphysics one is in danger of substituting speculation for knowledge. In everyday practice it's better to keep one's thinking strictly non-metaphysical. And I've now trained myself to do so quite instinctively. It is only when there is a knife about to cut one's throat within a few inches of one's face that one instinctively stops thinking in terms of anatomy and pathology.

Chapter 15

/\

At the same time every Saturday P., an old government official, used to seek me out for a little conversation. He was a charming old gentleman. He lived quietly and modestly off his pension, going for a four-hour walk every day, and occasionally spending all day sitting on a bench in the park by the river, looking contentedly in front of him and greeting politely the people who came to sit down on the bench beside him.

It was just that the actual conversation was a little difficult. For many years the old gentleman had suffered from delusions and hallucinations and for eighteen years he had had to be confined in an asylum because of a tendency for his actions to get out of control. However, there was no question of anything like that happening nowadays. He did no harm to anyone. Only his thought processes were rather peculiar. It was quite a business trying to follow them. Sometimes what he said seemed to make no sense at all. But he didn't mind if he wasn't understood. He was quite happy so long as one humoured him a little. What he liked best was for me to answer him in the same vein. A conversation with him would go something like this:

The old gentleman would begin:

'Ah, my dear doctor, I must ask you to give me your advice in a most troublesome matter. When the news of the raid broke the other day, I found I no longer had any difficulty in fastening my tendons to my cravat. That can happen to anyone of course. The next day, however, the garage owner's fiancé, whose profile is usually so very one-sided, scented the evangelical blossom of Whitsuntide before it had had any chance of smelling the Portuguese sauce. A most remarkable phenomenon, though I've known of it since the days of my ambidextrous contacts. You've heard of them, I dare say?'

Now it was for me to say something. So, I said:

'Only vaguely, Counsellor. Wasn't that the time those idiots wanted to depose Leo XIII for letting his Ninth Symphony get burnt?'

'But what nonsense you're talking, Herr Doctor! The Ninth Symphony wasn't burnt till much later. My ambidextrous studies were conducted at the time of the Second Dialectical Dynasty of Magnus Hirschfeld. It was just when the efforts at religious canalisation on the part of the starving hat-maker's unions were reaching their climax. You can deduce that from internal evidence in my works; I'll gladly lend them to you if you promise me to give up wearing braces.'

'Why braces exactly?'

'I have my reasons for that. It's been my consistent experience that space and time are hopelessly confused. There was a typical example of that this morning when I left my house to come and see you. One tram was going down the left-hand side of the road and another the right. Do you know what that means?'

'No, what?' I asked curiously. The old man leant over and whispered into my ear.

'Cause and effect. But I advise you to have nothing to do with it.'

'Is it so dangerous then?' I asked.

'What do you think?' he answered. 'No proselyte is going to stand for that forever. I was listening to the humming of our whole prehistoric situation on the Tentaphone long before sunrise this morning. It was no fun either as you can imagine. One's ear glued to that dreadful muddy river year after year without even being able to whistle! But I've renounced him now.'

'Who have you renounced?'

'The super-God. I can't let myself go on being sucked dry as if I were simply a melon. But what am I to do now? The thingummy won't answer and the temperature on the chart keeps rising. Now what I wanted to ask you, doctor, was this: working here in your slaughterhouse you have the best chance of observing the behaviour of the smaller swamp gods. What am I to do in future? Worship the hot water bottle or jump over the fence?'

'If you ask my advice, my dear Counsellor,' I told him, 'I should do neither. Go home and bide your time. More haste less speed, you know. In the meantime, don't go mixing-up cause and effect, or you'll get your dialectical headaches again and the super-God will suck you dry. And we don't want that to happen, do we? Be careful how you go then and don't trip over your thought-processes. You're not as young as you were, you know!'

'Thank you, dear doctor. You're the only person in this

whole wretched flower-pot who understands me. Goodbye!'

And he went out.

My secretary, a typical Berlin girl, had had to take this all down in short-hand. 'What on earth was that?' she said. 'It wasn't German, was it?'

'No,' I said. 'Schizophrenia.'

'And what's that all about—I mean what happens with schizophrenia?'

'I can't tell you that,' I answered. 'Perhaps it's the unconscious forcing its way through into the conscious.'

Chapter 16

M., the sculptor, was found dead in his house at ten o'clock in the morning. It was the charwoman who found him and she informed the police. A policeman from the local station established it as a case of suicide. He saw the bullet wound over the heart. The shot had passed through the white shirt front. The revolver lay beside the man's body. An empty bottle of champagne stood on a little table in front of him. The table lamp was still on. The sculptor had obviously taken his leave of life with a little celebration. He had even put on his dark suit. The charwoman said she had seen it coming: the gentleman was up to the eyes in debt, but every spring he had taken a trip to Rome. He had been hopeless about money. She had once listened at the door to a spirited conversation between him and his wife and she had distinctly heard him say: 'Then there's nothing left for me to do but kill myself.' His wife? Well, as a matter of fact he had had two wives.

When a death takes place without any witnesses the post-mortem has to be conducted by a police doctor. The policeman reported his find to me over the telephone and said that it was unquestionably a case of suicide.

The police car took me to a little villa on the outskirts of the town. There were two cypresses in the front garden but they didn't seem to be doing very well. In the house itself there was quite a collection of sculpture, vases, earthenware pots and tiles. I would have liked to have spent some time in front of each item examining it calmly. On the first floor I found an enormous studio with the famous artist's bedroom at the back.

There he lay on the big divan bed, with his head against the wall. He had presumably shot himself while sitting up and had then slipped slowly backwards. Everything was as the policeman had said on the telephone. 'A completely straightforward case,' he now repeated. 'This is how he must have pointed the gun.' He pointed a finger at his own heart. 'They say he was heavily in debt. And besides he was in domestic difficulties of some sort.'

I looked at the body. The hole in his shirt was plain enough. But if he had held the gun there his shirt would have been marked by the flash and there would also have been traces of powder. But the shirt around the bullet hole was white as snow. There was only a dark round hole over the heart and a thin line of dried blood running down his shirt front. Now, how did he manage to do that, I wondered. How far away is it possible to hold a revolver and shoot oneself without getting singed by the flash?

Carefully I lifted up the shirt which was stuck fast to the supposed bullet wound. I pushed my finger under the shirt. There was no bullet wound. The skin over the heart was unbroken. The policeman looked completely taken aback. I sat the corpse up and found the bullet wound behind the left ear, just above the back part of the skull.

'Well, I'm ...' said the policeman and his mouth fell open in astonishment.

'Exactly,' I said. 'Get on to the murder squad.'

The dead man couldn't have shot himself. Even someone who was left-handed couldn't shoot himself like that.

The policeman left the house. The sculptor hadn't been on the telephone. I was left alone with the charwoman. 'It was one of his women did that,' she said, 'I don't know which one, though.' She told me that the sculptor hadn't been married but had lived together for several years with a very beautiful woman of southern appearance. About a year ago he had fallen in love with a young girl who must have been at least thirty years younger than him. Ever since then there had been nothing but quarrels up to the very last day.

A quarter of an hour later the murder squad appeared with all their complicated technical apparatus. I testified that I had touched the body at two points but had then put it back in its original position. The revolver also lay where it had been found. Only the policemen had touched it. The charwoman made a statement. 'It must be the young one,' she said, 'the other one left for Rome some days ago.'

'If it was one of these two women who committed the murder,' said Detective Inspector G., the head of the murder squad, 'then it was certainly the older one, for she had her life behind her.' At that moment we heard the front door open and someone coming up the stairs. 'Well, now,' said the Detective Inspector, 'we'll soon see who shot him.'

We heard a voice on the landing:

'Good morning, Frau Müller. Where are you?'

'That's the young one,' said the charwoman softly.

'A completely straightforward case,' said the policeman. 'The old woman didn't want to give him up, so she shot him.'

A magnificent looking young girl came into the studio looking slightly surprised to see us. She took in what had happened at once. The charwoman began sobbing. The murder squad photographer who was sitting on the top of a huge ladder took a picture of the corpse from the ceiling The young woman turned deathly pale. She looked as if she were going to faint. The Detective Inspector took her arm and led her out of the room.

When she was interrogated it appeared that there had been an attempt at a *ménage à trois*. The sculptor had lived together with the other woman, who had been his model, for twenty years. It was plain from the young woman's evidence that theirs must have been a great love, but as the southern beauty was already over forty, her man needed 'something younger'. 'He was a very great artist,' said the girl. Martha, as the artist's old love was called, had wanted to give him up, but he wouldn't let her go. 'When you've lived together with someone for twenty years,' he had said, 'you can't simply go off like that.' In that case, Martha had said, he must get rid of the young girl. But he hadn't been able to do that and in any case she, the young girl, had refused to go. Then they had tried living together *à trois* but there had been perpetual quarrels. In the end the two women had agreed to force the man to decide between them. If he couldn't bring himself to decide for one or the other, they would both leave him. Thereupon he had made his decision for the young one and Martha had left for Rome. That had been some days ago.

'Now he's made it clear that he couldn't live without her,' concluded the young girl who in everything she said made a most open and honest impression. 'For me this shows that in the end he made his decision for the great love of his life. Martha proved stronger than me.'

The Inspector asked the girl why the man should have shot himself instead of going to Rome to get his friend back.

Martha wouldn't have come back,' said the girl. 'She was absolutely determined to bring this miserable life to an end once and for all. "When I go," she said, "I shall go for good. If he tries to get me back I shall shoot him."'

The Inspector now told her what had happened. one didn't seem surprised. When she was asked whether she thought it was Martha who had shot her friend, she made no answer. Another detective of the murder squad asked the Inspector if he should send out a hue and cry for Martha. But the girl cried out: 'You'll never get her. You don't think she'd let herself be tried for murder, do you? If not dead already, she'll kill herself the moment you try to lay hands on her.'

The Inspector was silent for a while. Then he said to his men: 'There's no hurry. We'd be too late in any case.'

That afternoon when I was back on duty at police head-quarters a woman who had tried to commit suicide was brought in to me. She had tried to hang herself in an attic. The rope was already round her neck when someone came in and found her. The alarm was given. The police were on the spot at once and took her in charge. She said that she was suffering from an incurable disease and had decided to do away with herself. She had no papers on her. She said her name was Elvira Meissner and that she had been born in a certain district of Dusseldorf. That was all she would say.

A message came in with her: 'To the police doctor on duty. Please state whether the prisoner is covered by paragraph ... of police regulations which permits the confinement to mental homes of persons dangerous to themselves or to the community.'

The prisoner was about forty years old, strikingly beautiful, with deep black eyes full of expression. Her face bore the marks of great sorrow. She said that she had been a secretary on a big estate in Pomerania but had given up the job when she became incurably ill. She had only a short time to live. She ought to be allowed to die.

'Don't you see that when someone is determined to die no one can stop them?' she said to me. 'And that no one ought to stop them?'

I told her that I would respect whatever grounds she might have for wanting to kill herself, but that it was out of the question for me to leave her to her fate.

'My fate,' she repeated and it seemed as if she was going to laugh. 'I've been left to my fate a long time now and you never bothered about me once. My fate is my own affair. So, now that it's too late you want to help me? I can't even bring myself to thank you.'

I said to her that she might feel she wanted to put an end to her life now but that no one could tell what she would feel like to-morrow. Experience showed that every sort of unhappiness could be got over in time, and so it was my duty to send her to the mental clinic where she wouldn't be able to kill herself. Time was a great healer, but it had to be given a chance to do its work.

She said that if I were to send her to the clinic I would make her ten times, a hundred times, more unhappy. Time could heal every sorrow but hers. 'You will be affronting the whole idea of liberty and human dignity if you have me shut up. Of course, all one can expect from a police official is that he should do his duty. But you're a doctor. You're a civilised man. You can't deprive me of my freedom of choice in this matter. Fate has given me all I could want from life—only to take it all away from me again. I've always had a deep respect for life, the respect I owe it as a human being who has loved it. I still have this respect for life. It's just because I know that I must hate life from now on that I don't want to go on living. To hate life, to hate beauty, to hate love, to hate God, if there is a God, would be too much, I couldn't bear it.'

At this instant I was prepared to let her go. I knew that it would cost me my job. But that didn't worry me. My only doubt was whether I was justified in letting the freedom of one individual take priority over the welfare of the community. If I were to let her go, she would soon try to kill herself again. Perhaps she would go straight out and throw herself under a car in front of police headquarters. The car might brake hard and get into a skid on the wet road. It might mount the pavement and kill a child. Or she would go home and turn on the gas. Then, when she was dead, someone would come into the gas-filled room with a lighted cigarette and there would be an explosion.

'A suicide is always a danger to the community,' I said, 'That's why I'll have to send you to the clinic.'

'Anything but that,' she begged me. 'If you don't trust me to put an end to my life without endangering others, then give me a fatal dose of morphia.'

'Where would we be if we gave everyone who wanted to kill themselves facilities to do so. I'm a doctor, not a murderer.'

This seemed to make an impression on her. She said nothing for a moment. Then:

'Even murder can be justified sometimes,' she said softly. 'But you can only think in paragraphs of the penal code and won't understand me when I say that there's an ethical duty which is far higher than one's ordinary social duty. One has a duty to kill someone who by making some monstrous mistake which he could have avoided, is about to bring his whole life's work to nothing. Suppose for instance that one of your bourgeois heroes, Beethoven if you like, after writing all his symphonies had been about to commit some despicable crime, and I had been the one who by murdering him had prevented him from doing so. You'd put up a statue to me for saving your hero from shame. You want to be able to honour your heroes. Would you honour Beethoven, would you be able to stand his music if you knew that he had committed some mean and filthy crime? If you knew that he had betrayed someone?'

I tried to think what to do. If she were to throw herself out of the window, it would not be I but the policeman sitting by the door who would have to bear the blame that he would just remain passively on his chair. But to my surprise and relief nothing happened.

I got on to the head of the murder squad on the telephone.

'You wanted to give Martha B. a start,' I said 'She made use of it too, but unfortunately she was caught in the act. She's here with me now. If I send her to the mental clinic will you proceed against her for murder?'

'I'm afraid I'll have to do that, doctor,' said the Inspector. 'But she had plenty of provocation. Well arrange matters so that she doesn't get a heavy sentence.'

'And what if I discharge her?'

'Then I'll have to get another police doctor.'

When the trial came on, the Inspector presented his case as if the sculptor had pressed the revolver into her hand. Even the judge accepted her condemnation of the murdered man. But Martha B. was out to condemn herself. She said that she had left him without a quarrel but had then gone back and shot him in cold blood from behind. There had been no quarrel between them at any time on the evening before the murder. She had shot him in revenge because he had abandoned her.

Martha B. received ten years' imprisonment. The Inspector took me home in his car after the trial. We spoke of out-of-date laws, wise judges and apparently hard-hearted prosecutors. I said I wondered whether, after this experience, one were really justified in trying to prevent a suicide from carrying out his or her purpose.

'Doctor,' said the Inspector, 'I don't think that human beings are justified in setting themselves up as arbiters of life and death in any circumstances. I have become convinced that this is where the limit to freedom of choice must lie. On this matter we submit ourselves blindly to a higher law, otherwise we relapse into the condition of Neanderthal man.'

'A higher law?' 1 asked. 'And what is that?'

'"Thou shalt not kill." We can't go beyond that.'

I wasn't unfamiliar with this point of view ,

'In France,' I said, 'Martha B. would have been set free.'

'The French,' he replied, 'can afford to free a murderess who has killed her lover in passion. But we don't live in France. If we Germans were to let a murderess go free, we would have established a precedent and before we knew where we were everyone would be killing everyone else. We're good at finding excuses for such things.'

'But it's still rather an extraordinary phenomenon: two such fundamentally different views of justice in two neighbouring countries. If a reporter from the Moon were to come to Earth and see that exactly the same murder ended in France with the release of the murderer and in Germany with her condemnation to ten years' imprisonment, he would write in his newspaper that there was no such thing as justice on Earth, and that men didn't know what they were about.'

'One would have to try and put the Moon newspaper right. Its reporter only sees the affair from the point of view of an outsider. In France all they see in a case such as Martha B.'s is the great love she upheld to the last. In Germany all we see is the breaking of an Old Testament law.'

'Martha B. not only upheld the sanctity of love,' I said, 'but also the sanctity of marriage as the basis of our society, that is if we overlook the fact that the sculptor and the murderess weren't officially married.'

'We've got to be clear in our minds about what is most worth saving if society is threatened: marriage or the rule of law.'

'I don't understand you, Inspector,' I replied. 'Like me you did everything you could to save Martha B. It's true we failed, but at least we tried. I find the sentence of ten years imprisonment unjust but you justify it.'

'All, my dear doctor,' said the Inspector, 'I'm a man of feeling. I distinguish between the sympathetic and unsympathetic murderer. And between a murder which I would be capable of committing myself and one against which my whole inner being revolts. Each of us, my dear doctor, might any day find ourselves in a situation in which we commit a murder of the type of Martha B.'s. That's why I wanted her to get off as lightly as possible, because it was myself I saw in the dock.'

Chapter 17

A government car fetched me from the clinic.

'We've got orders from the Minister of the Interior to take you to Neustadt. We need your opinion on a rather delicate matter.' Thus, I was informed by a gentleman sitting in the back seat of the car who introduced himself as a senior civil servant.

I couldn't conceal my astonishment at this extension of my powers. Up till now my responsibility had been confined to the provincial capital.

'Most unusual circumstances make your presence in Neustadt a matter of urgent necessity,' said the civil servant. 'We want your opinion on the mental state of a certain official there.'

I replied that in cases of this sort the district medical officer had to be consulted first. Neustadt was the chief town of its district and its medical officer, who was well spoken of and had had a psychiatric training, should be thoroughly qualified to pronounce on a person whose mental state was open to suspicion. The government would be well advised to call him in first and to consult me in a purely advisory capacity.

'And what if this medical officer is the man whose mental state needs to be enquired into?' asked the civil servant.

I said: 'Well, it's not every day that the one person in a district qualified to pronounce on such things becomes mentally ill himself. However, should Fate decide to play a practical joke of this sort I would suggest that the medical officer of the neighbouring district be called in to take over his job. Neustadt is only twenty-four kilometres away from the next district centre.'

'The medical officer from the neighbouring district is already in Neustadt,' said the civil servant.

'Well, everything's all right, then.'

'Unfortunately not. The medical officer of B. didn't come to Neustadt on government orders to take over his colleague's duties, but on his own initiative to give his colleague leave of absence owing to temporary unfitness for his post. He has appointed himself district officer of Neustadt in his place.'

'May I ask what the Neustadt District Council has to say to this?'

'Nothing. For in the meantime the medical officer of Neustadt has declared that the colleague who wished to depose him is himself of unsound mind and has ordered his confinement to a lunatic asylum.'

'I begin to see the difficult position the government is in,' I replied. 'So, in Neustadt at the moment there are two medical officers each declaring the other to be mad. And the Neustadt police are in the same position as Buridan's donkey: they don't know which one to take to the asylum.'

'Exactly,' said the civil servant. 'We received a telephone

message from Neustadt this morning saying that the police couldn't decide which of the two medical officers to send to the asylum. They didn't think it right to send both. You, my dear doctor, will have to decide for them.'

'Might I know something of the personal background of the two antagonists?' I asked.

'Both entered government service for the first time this year. The Neustadt man had been a surgeon in the North of Germany for twenty years. His younger opponent has had no specialist training but has spent some time as a youth psychiatrist.'

'Is it known why the Neustadt man gave up his surgeon's practice?' I asked. 'It's very unusual.'

'We don't know anything about that,' said the civil servant. 'We were short of doctors at the time and couldn't make as thorough enquiries into the backgrounds of the candidates as we would have liked.'

We arrived in Neustadt after a two-hour journey. Curiosity had brought a small crowd to the front of the town hall. Obviously, the news had spread that the two medical officers had declared each other mad, and that the police couldn't decide which to shut up.

The Chairman of the District Council received us.

'I'm in a most awkward situation, gentlemen,' he began, 'there's no reference to a case of this sort in the regulations. I have here two contradictory medical opinions. One of them must render the other invalid. Both doctors are properly declared to be of unsound mind and a danger to the community. But if I confine them both to an asylum then they both automatically become unfit for their posts and the certificates they have made out lose their validity. I really don't know what to do.'

The two medical officers were sitting in separate rooms complaining loudly about the policeman stationed in front of the door to see that they didn't escape. I first visited the medical officer from the neighbouring district to discover what had made him relieve his Neustadt colleague of his post. He said he had strong reason to suspect that his colleague was suffering from some mental disorder. His evidence came from the people of Neustadt themselves who had had an opportunity of observing their medical officer's eccentricities for months. He had several times fallen asleep in the middle of a consultation. Sometimes, after people who had made their applications to see him in the proper manner had been waiting for hours in the waiting room, he had come staggering in, asked them a few personal questions, talked a lot of nonsense and sent them home again. Only the day before, continued the medical officer from the neighbouring district, it had been reliably reported to him that his Neustadt colleague was raving round his offices, turning everything upside down and trying to 'inoculate against marriage complexes' those people who came to consult him about their marriage problems. As the nearest responsible medical officer, he had taken this as a cue to intervene and prevent further trouble. There had been no time to inform higher authority. Unfortunately, the Chairman of the Neustadt Council had let himself be confused by a counter-certificate made out by his unbalanced colleague.

I then went into the room where the other medical officer was waiting. He spoke perfectly calmly and logically. His colleague from the neighbouring district, he said, must obviously be off his head for he had come storming into his office while he was peacefully at work, and had declared in a loud voice that he (the Neustadt man) was suspended and was to consider himself under his orders from now on.

'I would indeed have been mad, if I had paid any attention to him,' he said.

His colleague had declared him to be of unsound mind on the strength of a vague report by some hysterical person to whom he had refused a state marriage allowance. The mad doctor had burst in on him like a lunatic, publicly in his own office. For the sake of his reputation, he had had no alternative but to take the strongest possible action against him. He regarded him as suffering from megalomania and had therefore sanctioned his immediate confinement to an asylum on the grounds of 'mania, paralysis, etc., etc.'

While he was talking to me, I noticed that his pupils were the size of pinpoints. I asked him to repeat his story to the senior civil servant sent down by the government. A police escort conducted him to an office on the first floor. Meanwhile I got two policemen to search his room. Hidden away at the back of his desk they found hundreds of empty phials of morphine. When he was asked to account for them the Neustadt medical officer strenuously denied all knowledge of them. He could only think they dated from the time of his predecessor.

He was now under suspicion as a drug addict. He assured us most vehemently and on his honour that he hadn't a single phial of morphine in his possession but when the police gave him a personal search, they found ten phials of morphine in the hollowed-out heel of his boot. Twenty-four more were found in a secret drawer. Meanwhile I sent a policeman off to the chemist to fetch the poison book. We established that since the one-time surgeon had set up a small private practice in Neustadt, ten times the amount of morphine had been prescribed as in the corresponding earlier period.

The senior civil servant released the zealous medical officer from B. from his painful situation and confirmed him in his new office in Neustadt. The morphine addict was taken out of the back door of the town hall to an ambulance. He was to be conveyed straight to the asylum. But he wouldn't get into the ambulance. When the police tried to force him, he over-ruled them saying that, by virtue of his powers as local medical officer, he was cancelling the order. He demanded that the matter should be referred to some higher author- ity. His own authoritative manner was so convincing and the respect in which he was held as a member of the educated classes was so great that the police became uncertain and let him alone for a moment. The cunning doctor seized the opportunity to escape. He ran round the building, jumped onto his motor bicycle and roared away. The village children showed us the way he had gone. They pointed towards the nearby frontier. The police informed the frontier post. But the fugitive didn't get as far as the frontier. Half-way there he crashed into a kilometre stone on his motor-bicycle and was thrown unconscious into a field. He woke up four days later in our clinic. He could remember nothing of the events in Neustadt which had preceded the accident. Indignantly he demanded his release. He then began to suffer from hallu- cinations, offering the pitiable spectacle of a human wreck whose moral character has been devoured by poison.

Character too is no more than an 'adjunct to the body'. It dissolves in alcohol or opium. I meant to write to my Orange Pastor about this, but somehow forgot.

Chapter 18

*The events of the previous chapter took place after Hitler had
made himself Dictator of Germany. His coming to power in 1933
must have made a great impression even on a young doctor who
had never concerned himself with politics. Or so I would have
thought, but I found no reference of any sort to the epoch-making
political events in Germany among these pages of Robert's. Of
course, one can't deduce anything from this about Robert's attitude to National Socialism.*

*But in the pocket diaries of those years in which Robert used
to jot down appointments, birthdays, journeys and also certain
accounts of events I did find something scribbled under the date
30ᵗʰ January 1933—a day admittedly of some historic interest—which showed that Robert had not quite overlooked it. The
entry ran:*

'Elfie back from skiing. Gave Bunty back. Hitler Chancellor of the Reich.'

Elfie was an actress friend of Robert's. She had a long-haired terrier called Bunty, which Robert looked after while its owner was away. Assuming that the order in which the events are recorded is not entirely accidental, one is forced to the conclusion that in Robert's mind his girlfriend's dog took precedence over politics. Things were soon to be very different.

Although he was a civil servant Robert was not a member of the National Socialist party. An excerpt from his writings, here taken out of its context, makes this quite clear:

We assistant doctors in the clinic were convinced that we would now have no alternative but to join the party. We were informed by a member of the Ministry of Health that there would be no future of any sort for those who, by their aloofness from the Party, showed their disapproval of the work being done for the reconstruction of Germany. We therefore agreed to join the Party in a body so that it would not be possible later on for anyone to think that he had been passed over for promotion on political grounds. This decision was taken unanimously although there wasn't one of us who didn't have his anxieties on enquiring about the duties which membership of the Party would entail. It appeared that we would have to put in a regular attendance at Party meetings.

The collective transfer to the Party of all assistants in the clinic was quite a little ceremony. The local Party organiser, whose jurisdiction we came under, had decided not to address us himself but to bring in a well-educated speaker from outside to explain to us the significance of the step we were taking. He was careful not to employ the usual jargon-ridden slogans of the day with which we were all so familiar from newspapers, broadcasts and posters. He spoke in a quiet matter-of-fact way about the great tasks which the Führer was undertaking for the glory of Germany. When he came on to the Jewish problem, there was a distinct stir of unrest among us, for one of our most senior doctors was a Jew, and he was a man whom we all loved and respected. The Party speaker said it wasn't going to be easy for the Führer to solve the Jewish problem, but he was determined to settle it 'one way or another'. Then he went on: 'Of course all Jews could be sent to some island where they would all be together. But what then is to be done about the people who are only partly Jewish?' Without a moment's hesitation I shouted out across the hall: 'They could be sent to a peninsula!' A certain amount of confusion was immediately noticeable among the uniformed gentlemen on the platform. When the rest of the clinic doctors were taken into the Party in a body two of us were turned away. I was told that I didn't yet possess the maturity required of a member of the Party. The other exception was Dr Stöhr. 'What did you do wrong?' I asked him when the ceremony was over. 'I laughed,' he replied, and he didn't even seem to hold it against me.

Four years after this abortive attempt to join the Party— Robert Vossmenge never tried again—he received a visit in his office from Pastor Degenbrück.

Pastor Degenbrück brushed aside the words with which I welcomed him. He looked at me searchingly, touched the lapel of my coat and said:

'So, you're not a member of the Party, Doctor?'

I shook my head.

'Do you have anything to do with the sterilisation of the unfit?' he asked me straight out.

I answered that I had taken part in sessions of the racial hygiene commission from time to time, as adviser or observer.

'And what, may I ask, is your attitude to the idea, as a Christian?'

'What has Christianity got to do with sterilisation of the unfit?' I countered.

'A great deal, Doctor—more than you seem to think. Do you remember our conversations about the principles of psychiatry, and how I saw psychiatry as a ruthless impersonal force?'

'Of course I do,' I said. 'I even thought I had partly managed to convert you to a different view.'

'The sterilisation laws are based on the ideas of a psychiatrist called Rüdin. Years ago, a psychiatrist called Hoche recommended euthanasia. One day the Anti-Christ will adopt this idea as well as a cloak for his own unspeakable crimes. God preserve us from psychiatry!' shouted Pastor Degenbrück. Fortunately, the doors of my consulting room were very thick and I didn't have to worry about our conversation being overheard.

'No one's said anything about euthanasia,' I replied, 'so let's leave that to your own ghoulish imagination. As for legal sterilisation, what you don't seem to know is that it was introduced into certain states of North America as long ago as 1908. Certain European countries followed their example soon afterwards. It is even permitted in certain circumstances in some of the cantons of freedom-loving Switzerland.'

'And what happens in freedom-loving Switzerland when an unfit person doesn't want to be sterilised?' asked the Pastor.

'The question doesn't arise since sterilisation can only take place there on the application of the person concerned or on that of his or her legal guardian, and it has to be sanctioned by a commission of specialists.'

'And on whose application is it done here?'

'Also on that of the person concerned, or his or her guardian, or that of the district medical officer.'

'And what happens if the commission sanctions sterilisation on the application of the district medical officer, and the person concerned doesn't agree to it?'

'The sterilisation then takes place compulsorily,' I said, 'but we set considerable store by trying to convince the patient of the suffering he would cause if he were allowed to beget children who in their turn would perhaps suffer from his disease. You asked me what my attitude to sterilisation was as a Christian. Well, this is what I think. You may not regard it as a Christian attitude according to your definition, for you, my dear Pastor, stick literally to the words of the Bible: "Take ye wives and beget sons and daughters." You seem to interpret this as if it meant: "Take ye wives and beget as many sons and daughters as you can even though some of them may be mentally deficient." I can't share this view. Before the days of the sterilisation laws, nothing was known about this aspect of genetics. That is why the founders of our religion, who couldn't know about the developments of modern science, ignored the subject of racial hygiene. But to-day we can't ignore it any longer. The Church shouldn't stick so closely to the letter of religion. By doing so it lays itself open to charges of reaction.'

'The Church unfortunately didn't get a chance to clarify its reactionary attitude to sterilisation. It wasn't consulted when the law was made. The law is concerned solely with the hygienic aspects of the matter. But the carrying-out of the law makes a number of quite unjustifiable psychiatric assumptions.'

'What do you mean?'

'That's just what I've come here to explain, Doctor. Do you remember a cynical remark of one of your doctors about normal man being merely a harmless imbecile?'

'I remember telling you about it.'

'Well, the sterilisation laws have a clause covering imbecility. Is it the whole of humanity you want to exterminate, Doctor?'

'The law is of course only applied in serious cases of hereditary imbecility,' I said. I felt slightly uneasy.

'Can you tell me, my dear Doctor, where plain physiological stupidity ends and pathological imbecility begins? Are there special characteristics which you could establish as symptoms of imbecility in a scientific diagnosis?'

'That unfortunately is the weakness of the law,' I said. 'We have to fall back on a relatively arbitrary test. To give uniformity to that test the law provides for a questionnaire to be filled out by the individual concerned and to be put in with the other papers.'

'And this questionnaire includes, for instance, the question: "Who was Bismarck?" Do you realise, Doctor, that there are peasants living on the Masurian lakes in East Prussia who have never heard of Bismarck?'

'That's not the only question in the questionnaire. Besides it isn't necessarily the correctness of the answer which determines the diagnosis.'

'And doesn't the questionnaire also contain the question: "What causes night and day?" Do you realise, Doctor, that there are peasants living at the back of the Masurian lakes who couldn't tell you what causes night and day?'

'That depends of course on what they were taught in school.'

'Ah, now I've caught you, Doctor. The schools in East Prussia are no worse than anywhere else in Germany. But there aren't enough of them. The country is very sparsely inhabited. Only twenty years ago the children had to walk for hours to get to school. Many of these peasants can hardly write their names. Of course, they don't know who Bismarck was. And though they probably do know why night follows day, they couldn't put the reason down on paper. And so, my dear Wind Doctor, these peasants have been sterilised against their will by compulsory methods utterly unworthy of any civilised state.'

'I don't believe it,' I said indignantly. 'The district medical officers must know their peasants. Even if a medical officer were, out of excessive zeal, to order sterilisation in such an utterly unjustifiable case, the commission would still be there to act as a check on the case.'

'You forget, my dear Doctor, that the peasants didn't know who Bismarck was. And one must know that. Particularly these days. Besides until recently there weren't all that number of medical officers in East Prussia. Many of the posts had been vacant for years. So, a number of young doctors who had only just passed their exams had to be sent to fill them. A raw young advocate was appointed as chairman of the racial hygiene commission. None of these gentlemen had ever been to East Prussia before. True to the oath they had sworn to safeguard the progeny of the German people they decided to sterilise the peasants of the Masurian lakes.'

'I simply don't believe it,' I said angrily. 'Although I admit that the questionnaire has its defects.'

'I thought your idealism would probably be proof against all criticism. So, I've brought the evidence along with me.'

Pastor Degenbrück handed me a photostat of a letter from the Prussian Minister of the Interior to all government authorities in East Prussia. This letter stated that the 'systematic unjustifiable sterilisation of the old-established peasantry of East Prussia' had led to complaints being made to the Minister by high officials of the Ministry of Agriculture. The Minister ordered an immediate enquiry which was to be conducted in secret. 'The local Party branches entrusted with the enquiry are to answer to me personally for the fact that nothing seeps through to the public.'

'Apart from the poor syntax and the tragic fate of the Masurian peasantry, what do you think of that, my dear doctor?'

'And what transpired at the enquiry? And what happened to the doctors?'

'The systematic unjustifiable sterilisation of the old-established peasantry of East Prussia was brought to an end. But no one dared to bring the young doctors from the Rhineland to trial. That would have meant a scandal. They were sent home to their peasants in the Rhineland, who of course knew all about Bismarck. Yes, you're right, Doctor, normality is equivalent to mild imbecility. Only this time it's your official colleagues from the Rhineland I'm referring to. In my opinion the law governing the sterilisation of the unfit should apply equally to them.

'Isn't it ludicrous? Our Führer wants a healthy people. He says that the future lies with a healthy race. He distributes state marriage allowances, children's allowances and all the time his henchmen are going about sterilising the peasants because they don't know who Bismarck was. Psychiatry is stronger even than the will of the Führer. For you, Doctor, the law governing the sterilisation of the unfit rests on strictly scientific principles. You think you know what imbecility is. But you're mad yourself to think so. Admit that you're just as mad as the wretched people you sterilise. You're a far worse case than those you've so often told me about. Take that old woman in your clinic, for instance, who thought her son was being tortured down in the cellar. What a harmless form of madness hers was compared with yours. Go and get yourself sterilised, Doctor!'

He shouted these last words so loudly that my secretary came hurrying in.

'What's going on in here?' she asked.

'Do you know who Bismarck was?' Pastor Degenbrück shouted at her.

'Of course I do,' she answered sharply.

'Well, you're lucky then,' cried the Pastor, and without another word he turned and left the room.

'And you're letting him walk around free, Doctor?'

'He's absolutely right. We're all mad,' I said. I felt in that moment as if I was falling from the top of a high tower.

'What's Bismarck got to do with it?' asked the girl.

'Do you really know who Bismarck was?' I asked, and I put particular emphasis on the word 'really'.

'All I know is that he was the Iron Chancellor, but I don't know who he really was,' she said. 'We all know too little.'

'Yes,' I agreed. 'That's the trouble. We know too little.'

Chapter 19

On the edge of the big park lay the magnificent villa of Herr Perkuhner, the chairman of a large silk-manufacturing firm. The chairman had allowed me to continue my official examination of him in his own home. So far, this examination had yielded no results at all. He was a much-travelled well educated gentleman of the old school, and in the course of a long conversation in my office he had talked with considerable charm but had shown no sign of mental disorder at all. He skillfully turned all questions about his domestic affairs. If he really was mentally ill, as his family maintained, he was still nimble-witted enough to be able to avoid disclosing his madness to strangers.

Was there in fact anything wrong with him? Looking at the hideous villa from the outside, I had remembered a little shop-keeper who had once appeared in my office. He had wanted advice about the best way of getting his mentally sick wife into an asylum. His wife, he said, pestered him night and day with sexual lighting equipment which she had had built into the walls of his house 'to exhaust him'. During the day when he was in the shop, she used the radio or the water pipes for the same purpose. He simply couldn't get away from her and implored me to shut her up. How disappointed the man was when not his wife, but he, was sent off to a mental home! Might not there be something similar about the case of Herr Perkuhner?

As I approached the magnificent glass-roofed entrance, I recalled the few facts I had gleaned from the chairman's family lawyer in the course of our last conference. The Perkuhners, husband and wife, had been living apart for a long time now. They corresponded with each other only through the lawyer. The lady of the house lived on the second floor, the chairman himself on the first. The old man had let off the ground-floor rooms to the Party as a set of offices. The Party profited to good effect from Herr Perkuhner's estrangement from his family. At regular intervals he made very considerable contributions to their funds. Perkuhner's heirs already saw themselves deprived of some half a million marks, the lawyer told me. The more mistrustful of his family the old man became, the greater were his contributions to Party funds.

At the entrance there was one bell for 'Max Perkuhner' and another for 'Maria Perkuhner'. I rang the first. After a few minutes Max Perkuhner opened the door and led me up to the first floor. We went up a wide marble staircase lined with heavy banisters. Bright stained-glass windows let in fragments of daylight. On the first floor there was a large dark landing. On the left the stairs went up to the second floor, on the right was a wooden partition. My reaction to this wooden partition was that of a Big Game hunter who comes across the fresh tracks of a rhinoceros. Admittedly the war had been going on for two years now and raw materials were short, but a rich man who was able to contribute something like a fortune to the Party every month could have done better for himself than to erect a cheap fence of wooden boards in the middle of the grandest part of his house.

'And did you put up the wooden partition yourself?' I asked him.

'In my family,' answered the chairman, 'it was a tradition that we should all learn a trade before we went into the business. My father had me trained as a carpenter.' He tapped lightly on the wall. 'You wouldn't think it was several decades since I had last held a tool in my hands, would you?'

'A masterpiece, sir,' I said. 'But where's the door?'

'Doors are dangerous. They let one's enemies in,' said Herr Perkuhner. 'So why have doors?' And he pushed away a piece of the partition which revealed itself as the back of an enormous sideboard. Then the old man slipped in through the gap and disappeared.

'Please come in, Herr Doctor,' I heard him call out of the darkness. 'Welcome to my fortress.'

My reason told me to be careful and not to follow the madman into his den. But professional curiosity was too strong. I forced myself through the narrow opening and heard the old man wheezing and groaning as he pushed the sideboard back in front of the opening again.

'Now we'll have some light. Please excuse this miserable reception, but it's war-time you know, and electricity has to be saved, so I switched off the chandelier when I left the room to open the door to you.'

A magnificent blaze of light immediately appeared from a glittering crystal chandelier above our heads. I looked round the fortress. I found myself in a veritable arsenal.

'Permit a keen old sportsman to show you his most precious treasures. This fine shot-gun here will help me to give a good account of myself against the Führer's enemies when they come for me. Both barrels are loaded with ball and buckshot.'

He placed the barrels of his shot-gun against my chest with a mocking smile. 'This is where the Führer's enemies will meet their end and that is where they'll be made into sausage meat.' He pushed open a door into the kitchen. The shutters were closed but in the feeble light which filtered through them a number of pots could be seen on the stove.

Suddenly he started boring the barrels of his shotgun painfully into my chest:

'I know who you are, Doctor, you're an enemy of the Führer. My wife sent you here. Admit that you're sent here as a spy by my family!'

'An excellent defensive position,' I answered evasively. 'I must express my admiration. Did you serve with the engineers, sir?'

'No with the Cuirassiers. We were His Majesty Kaiser Wilhelm II's favourite regiment. I took part in the last full-dress parade in 1914. Would you like to see my breastplate? I've still got it.'

He was still aiming his gun at me.

'It would give me the greatest pleasure, sir,' I said. 'Ah, those were the days, when the Cuirassiers were the guardians of the old Reich.'

The old man finally put his gun down on a magnificent French baroque chest of drawers. He opened a glass cabinet and pulled out a shining piece of armour.

'Excuse me a moment, Doctor, it's a long time since I had it on.'

He took the breast-plate in his right hand, the shot-gun in his left and disappeared into another room. I cast a quick glance into the room after him. I saw that the walls were lined to the ceiling with book-shelves.

This was my chance to try and get out through the hole in the partition again. I had no wish to be made into sausage meat. I tried to push the side-board away, but without success. I pushed at it with all my strength. It wouldn't move.

The old man was suddenly standing beside me again.

'You wish to leave already, Doctor? You haven't yet seen my collection of arms. Besides you'll never get out of my fortress like that. There's a secret catch which makes it impossible for the piece of furniture to be moved. I had to install this as a security measure, to stop anyone getting in from outside.'

'You've thought of everything, sir,' I said. 'Can you show me how this secret device of yours works?'

'My dear Doctor, I know you think I'm mad, but I'm not so mad that I'm going to show you how to get out of here.'

And he smiled as if he had made a joke.

'Unfortunately, my breast-plate is too tight for me these days, but I'm delighted to think that there are still people who remember the Cuirassiers. The only thing I don't believe is that you ever once saw them in your life. You're much too young to have seen the Cuirassiers. You must be a spy!'

I now pretended to feel insulted.

'Herr Perkuhner,' I said sharply, and my tone was not without its effect, 'until this moment it hasn't occurred to me that there was anything the matter with you. But now for the first time I begin to doubt your reason. What proof have you that I am an enemy of yours? You know that I am a civil servant, a high-ranking civil servant of the State of which the Führer is the head, and for which he is fighting against

133

overwhelming odds. The Führer wouldn't have a chance if his own civil servants were opposed to him and his friends. You want to make sausage-meat of me? Simply on suspicion? You're making a very serious mistake, let me tell you. It will do you no good. Just think for a moment: the police of course know that I am here. If I don't return alive this evening they'll come and look for me. Then they—and remember they are the Fuhrer's police—will break into your fortress and free me dead or alive. Look what you will have done. By your own stupidity you will have brought about a situation which it was beyond the power of your enemies to accomplish. Your fortress will be wide open and the next night...' I stopped for a moment, wondering how on earth to go on.

'The next night? Yes, go on! What will happen the next night, Doctor?'

He stared at me; his face tortured by anxiety.

'It will be to-night,' I said mysteriously.

'The attack? To-night? Well, Doctor, I shall sell my life dearly I can tell you. I'm well-armed. If you're a friend of the Fuhrer's, then help me to defend my fortress. The Fuhrer will be in the gravest danger if I am killed. You must stand by me. Do you know how to use a hand grenade?'

'Hand grenades won't be any good. The enemy have gas. There's nothing we can do against them.'

'And what about the anti-tank defences?' he countered with a triumphant smile. 'How are they going to break through the anti-tank defences?'

'What anti-tank defences?' I asked.

'The anti-tank defences which the Party has put up round here.'

'I didn't see any,' I said. 'Where are they supposed to be?'

'The Party has assured me that they have constructed a

set of anti-tank ditches. It's cost me a great deal of money. I haven't noticed any either but perhaps they've put them outside the grounds. I must say I would have preferred it if they'd put them round the house itself.'

'Well, there are no anti-tank ditches round the house,' I said, 'You would have seen where the earth had been displaced. You couldn't help noticing that. But anti-tank defences on the other side of the grounds won't be of any use to us.'

'Why not?' asked the old man.

'Because one day the enemy is going to drop here by air. What have you in the way of anti-aircraft?' I said as if I were his military superior.

The chairman threw himself down in an Empire chair and stared glumly ahead of him.

'We're done for,' he said. 'I've done nothing about anti-aircraft defences.'

'We've still got a chance,' I said. 'But you must put yourself entirely in my hands, or we will be done for.'

'The Führer's enemies won't get me,' he said, and his face took on an expression of grim determination. 'I shall defend myself here until I drop. But you can go. Give my respects to the Führer and warn him for me.'

Then he pulled back a hidden iron bolt from the partition, removed a heavy block in front of the sideboard, pushed the sideboard away and motioned to me to leave.

But I couldn't just leave the madman to his fate like this.

'But what do you hope to be able to do with that old shot-gun of yours and your buck-shot?' I asked him. 'You won't even hear them coming. They'll drop down here in the grounds without a sound, on this side of the anti-tank ditches. Then equally quietly they'll creep up round your position, break one of the windows and fill the place with poison gas. You won't get a chance to fire a single shot!'

'What am I to do then, Doctor?' he asked desperately. 'Forgive me for taking you for an enemy of the Führer's at first. I see now that you're the only one who can help me. At least you don't think I'm mad. You too believe that the enemies of the Führer will come and attack me here one night. My wife doesn't understand me. The only thing she ever says is: Max, don't you see, you're suffering from persecution mania? Doctor, am I suffering from persecution mania?'

'Don't pay any attention to what your wife says,' I replied. 'Women don't understand the subtleties of politics. The Führer has many more enemies in the world than are good for him, and we must see how we can get out of here. You're an old soldier, sir. What does Clausewitz advise when a position is no longer tenable?'

'An elastic withdrawal. But where shall I withdraw to? My enemies are everywhere. I don't feel myself safe anywhere.'

'Trust to me. I'll take you to a safe hide-out where your enemies will never find you.'

'But what if they do find me?' asked the old man anxiously.

'In the meantime, we'll see what we can do to prevent their attack altogether.'

'All right, then, Doctor, I'll go with you. I'm deeply grateful to you. May I mark the occasion in a small way? Please accept this breast-plate as a token of my gratitude.'

'Thank you. We'll see about that later. But now we must think about getting you to safety. Come on.'

The sick man hung up his gun carefully in the cupboard, after first putting on the safety catch. He packed up a small suitcase with a few necessities. Then he left the house with me. It was already getting dark when we arrived at the clinic. 'This is the mental clinic,' I said. 'Your enemies will never

136

think of looking for you here.'

'Thank you, Doctor,' said the old man. Then one of the attendants took him off to the refractory block. He gave me one last friendly wave before the door shut behind him.

Chapter 20

Back in the office I dictated my report on the dangerous mental condition of the chairman of the silk company, Max Perkuhner, and took it in to my boss for signature. Ever since the beginning of the war our office had, in special cases, had the right to confine lunatics on its own responsibility without a judicial warrant. But such action could only be taken by the head of the Public Welfare Department himself. Perkuhner was a well-known figure in the town and my boss read the report through particularly carefully.

'Have you been able to make a diagnosis?' he asked me.

'I assume progressive paralysis, accompanied by paranoia and powerful megalomania.'

When the report had been passed and signed, I went back to my office and rang up the Perkuhner family lawyer to tell him what we were doing. The lawyer begged me to wait for him in my office as he had something important to say to me which couldn't be said over the telephone. I promised to wait for him.

He came sooner than I had expected. He gave a searching look at my secretary, then shut the double doors carefully behind him and put his hat over my telephone. 'You never can tell,' he said and drew me into a corner of my consulting room. For a moment I half expected him too to ask me if I were an enemy of the Fuhrer's. Paranoia can often spread from those who are mentally unbalanced to perfectly healthy people. This sort of induced madness is by no means rare among those who spend a lot of time in the company of lunatics.

'The Perkuhner family are deeply obliged to you, doctor,' said the lawyer. 'But for your intervention the whole of the rest of the family fortune would have gone.'

'What I can't understand,' I said, 'is why you, as the Perkuhner family's legal adviser, didn't long ago make an application to the court to have the old man declared *non compos mentis*?'

'Of course, I made such an application—over six months ago,5 said the lawyer.

'And it hasn't been granted yet? The courts don't usually take so long in these cases.'

'I had my application rejected eight days later, without any reason being given.'

'I can't understand that.'

'I couldn't understand it myself at first. Now I do. I asked one of the judges privately what could have happened.'

'You make me curious,' I said.

'Can't you really guess what made the court reject the application?' he asked me.

'You mean, the Party ...'

'But who else, Doctor?' His voice sank to a whisper. 'We

were about to deprive the Party of the goose which laid the golden eggs. The Party told the court that if it declared the old man Perkuhner unfit to manage his estate, all the judges concerned would find themselves in a concentration camp.'

'A pleasant prospect for us,' I said, 'For by officially consigning Perkuhner to a mental clinic we've temporarily deprived him of the power to manage his estate. So, the goose can't lay any more eggs.'

'You'll have to look out for a few days, doctor,' said the lawyer. 'That's what I wanted to warn you about.'

'I'm not afraid of the Party,' I said. 'I'm no paranoiac.'

'I think you underestimate these people, doctor,' said the lawyer. 'What will you do if the Party proclaims you an enemy of the Führer?'

The next morning it seemed best not to get to the office too early. It wasn't until midday that I rang up my secretary to ask what the news was.

'Nothing special,' she said. 'The boss has been arrested.'

'Thanks,' I said. 'Is that all? Then I won't be in till later.'

Calmly I packed up a suitcase, as if I were going away, and went to a hotel by the station. Later in the afternoon I rang up my secretary again from a public call box.

'What's the news?' I asked her.

'Sorry, wrong number,' she answered and hung up.

I could only assume that there was someone waiting for me in my office who had no business to be there.

I took the tram to the local army administrative H.Q. In the ante-room of the medical section was an extremely intelligent, brown-eyed girl with whom I had always got on very well. Right at the beginning of the war I had been classified as 'reserved' but from time to time I was sent for by the local administrative headquarters to be told that I could expect to be called up within a few days. My boss, however, had some-how always managed to have my calling up postponed.

Fortunately, I found this girl alone in her office when I went in to see her.

'You're the only person who can save me from a concentration camp,' I said, and I told her what had happened. 'You must have me called up at once.'

The girl didn't have to think for long.

'It so happens that we've got a demand for a replacement in from Italuft.'

'Italuft?' I interrupted her. 'What's that?'

'Italuft's the headquarters of the General Officer Commanding the Luftwaffe in Italy—they're responsible for North Africa.'

'Can't you send me off to North Africa as a replacement?' I asked. 'It's just the sort of post I'm looking for.'

'Unfortunately, we sent a replacement off yesterday,' she said.

'That's a pity. So, I'm a day too late?'

'I'm sure they can do with one more medical officer in North Africa,' said the girl. 'Of course, it isn't certain that the Senior Medical Officer here would approve my recommendation. But then he's away at the moment!'

'But surely some high-up has got to sign my travel orders?' I said. 'Or can you sign for the Senior Medical Officer?'

'The Senior Medical Officer's Assistant is in charge here while he's away. Although he doesn't like to do anything without asking his superior first ... But wait a minute, I've got an idea: the Senior Medical Officer's Assistant has a weakness for heroes. Tell him that you want to get to the front at once. You could never look your children in the face again if you had to spend the whole of the rest of the war here behind the lines. It's a matter of honour for you to shed your blood for the Fatherland. Go on like that at him until you beat him to his knees. In the meantime, I'll be getting your papers ready. Look out, here he comes.'

The Senior Medical Officers' Assistant came into the room. I jumped up from my chair and stood stiffly to attention. He saluted in an offhand way without looking at me.

'This is Doctor Vossmenge,' said the girl. 'He's from outside. He wants to get to the front.'

The Senior Medical Officer's Assistant, a Major, looked at me in a way which was not unfriendly. 'Glad to hear it,' he said. 'But wait until you're called up.'

'We've got a demand in from Italuft for a replacement for North Africa. As he seems to be in a hurry, I thought perhaps ...'

'We can wait until the Senior Medical Officer comes back for that.'

'I most humbly beg the Major's pardon,' I said, still standing to attention, 'but I can't stay here on the home front any longer. Like all Germans I have a right to take an active part in the defence of my Fatherland. The war has been going on for two years now. I haven't yet been to the front. How am I going to be able to look my children in the face when they ask me what I did in the war, and where my medals and my wounds are? Must I tell them that I spent the whole war with a soft job behind the lines? Major, one of my ancestors fought with Gustavus Adolphus in the Thirty Years' War, another fell at Issum in the War of the Spanish Succession, my grandfather took part in the storming of the Düppel redoubt, six of my mother's brothers spent four years in Flanders and before Verdun. Who will stop me from offering up my life—if only as a medical officer—for the glory of the Fatherland?'

143

There were tears in my eyes. I had even moved myself. My words had their effect. The Major seized my right hand in both of his, shook it vigorously, looked me straight in the eye and said:

'You shall have your way, if I can do anything about it. While there are still men like you about, I know there is no need to fear for the future of Germany.'

Then to the brown-eyed girl who was staring at my tears in amazement he said:

'Fräulein Ema, get the doctor's papers ready. He can go off to a reserve detachment to-day to get his uniform and equipment. And by to-morrow evening he can be in Rome reporting to Italuft.'

The girl had already made out the papers. The Major now seemed to take for granted the speed with which everything was done. He signed the papers and shook hands with me.

I left the town by the next train without saying good-bye to any of my friends. It took longer than I had anticipated to draw my clothing and equipment from the reserve detachment at P., which was the equipment centre for all doctors going to the southern theatre of war. Apparently, it was essential that I should report to the commanding officer of the medical section. He appeared during the afternoon, a remarkably young doctor with the rank of Major. He was about twenty-six years old and accompanied by a dachshund. When he had gone into his office, the Sergeant-Major made us parade outside in the rickety wooden corridor. The building had formerly been the stables of the Schloss at P. where Queen Marie of Rumania had lived. We waited about in the corridor for an hour or so and then the Sergeant-Major came out of the office and roared 'Dismiss!' I could see the young medical Major in the middle of the room playing with

144

his dachshund. He had no time to spare for someone like me who was so anxious to get to the front.

The next morning we were woken at six o'clock. I received my travel papers. But my military identity card was to be given to me by the young Major himself, though I would gladly have foregone this privilege. Again, we stood about on the uneven floor over the old stables. The young Major and his dachshund appeared at eleven. He had a wonderful way of ignoring the people waiting for him outside his office. Eventually the farewell ceremony began. We were called in by the Sergeant-Major in pairs. A corporal and I, now wearing the uniform of a Lieutenant in the Medical Corps, went in together.

'Corporal Müller back from leave, sir!' reported the Corporal.

The medical Major played with his dachshund and took no notice of the man.

While I was wondering what the point of this ceremony could be the corporal disappeared and the Sergeant-Major led me forward, saying:

'Your report!'

What on earth was I to report? My mind was a blank. I took a step forward, saluted and roared:

'Corporal Vossmenge back from leave, sir!'

The Major continued to play with his dog.

The Sergeant-Major said: 'Dismiss.'

I received my identity card and was now free to go off to the war.

I reached Munich in an hour. The troop train left Munich central for Rome just after seven in the evening. We passed through the Brenner about midnight. I felt safer now. But I still had the feeling that I had forgotten about something.

As the train roared on down the valley of the Esch I kept on wondering what this was. Then I realised: I should have sent the young Major and his dachshund off to the mental clinic.

Italuft, the headquarters of the General Officer Commanding the Luftwaffe in Italy, was situated in the Via Borelli, near the University. Two twelve-storey blocks of flats of the type that were being put up in considerable quantities all over the outskirts of Rome at that time, had been taken over, and the internal walls had been knocked through to accommodate the General's gigantic staff. Since Rome had been declared an open city and our Italian allies didn't want any German soldiers within its walls, only civilian clothes could be worn. Soldiers on leave however or who, like me, were in transit, wore uniform. My travel papers only took me as far as Rome. Here I was to receive fresh instructions for my journey to North Africa as a replacement for a medical corps Captain called von Behm. The Sergeant-Major on duty looked through my papers. Then he said.

'You can look round Rome for a bit this afternoon. You'll be going back to Munich to-night.'

'Can't I fly to North Africa, then?' I asked.

'What do you think this is: a travel agency?' he answered. 'There's been some mistake about you. We've already sent two men off as replacements for Captain von Behm. You'll be going back to Munich to-night. That's all there is to it.'

'But don't you have to get this confirmed?' I asked.

The Sergeant-Major ignored the question, picked up my papers, went across to another office and left me to wait outside. After a few minutes I was called in to see a medical corps Major. I gave him a regulation salute.

'Have you been to Rome before?' asked the Major.

I said I hadn't.

'Then stay another day here and take a look round the city. To-morrow evening you'll be going home again. As you've been told, you were sent here by mistake.'

'Excuse me, Major,' I said. 'I'd rather not go back to Germany.'

And I gave him a detailed account of what had happened to me during the last few days. He listened attentively. Then he said:

'It would be no use sending you to North Africa. All troops for North Africa are being held at Naples. No one's going across at the moment. The latest reports are that Rommel has been beaten and that the Africa Corps is withdrawing westwards. We'll be lucky if Rommel avoids capture. The British have come round in his rear from the desert. If the battle goes against us, you'd be sent back to Germany from Naples anyway.'

I said: 'Well, I don't want to go back to Germany, I've had enough of that.'

'Now don't be silly, my dear fellow. Wait a minute though, perhaps I've got a way out.' He thought for a moment. 'There's a Luftwaffe hospital in Catania. The doctor in charge is an old friend of mine. Go and report there. Tell him the story you've just told me. Perhaps he'll help you. If not, you can always jump into Etna.' He pressed a bell. The Sergeant-Major came in. 'Sir?'

'Give the Lieutenant travel papers for Catania. He's been seconded to the Luftwaffe hospital there. Once again, you've misread the original set of papers. See that it doesn't happen again. Thank you.'

He tore up the first set of papers which detailed me as a replacement for Captain von Behm in North Africa. He tore them into tiny little pieces and let them flutter out of the window. In Rome there's always a fresh breeze blowing in from the sea. The pieces of paper rose high into the air. We watched them for some time.

The doctor in charge of the Luftwaffe hospital at Catania received me the day I arrived. I gave him his friend's regards from Rome and told him my story.

'I'm afraid I can't help you,' he said to me eventually. 'Communications with the front in North Africa are at a standstill. Rommel must have been taken prisoner by the British by now. What do you want to get over there for? The war was lost ages ago. You can do anything you like but you can't stay here in the hospital.'

In the hospital orderly room, the Sergeant-Major said to me:

'What's going to happen to you now? Have you got orders to go to North Africa?'

'No,' I said, 'I haven't got any orders.'

'That's just not possible in the army,' said the Sergeant-Major. 'Have you been allotted to us?'

'No, not that either,' I said. 'I assure you I haven't any orders at all.'

'That's simply not possible. You've just got to do what your superior officer tells you. Of course, orders are sometimes wrapped up in rather vague language and aren't always easy to understand. Now, just repeat to me what the C.O. said.'

'I assure you, he gave me no instructions at all. He simply said the war was ... yes, well, he said: do what you like but you can't stay here.'

'There you are,' said the Sergeant-Major. 'A perfectly clear order. I'll give you ration cards for the Italian restaurants. They're valid for three weeks.'

'I don't understand what you're talking about,

Sergeant-Major.'

'You've got to carry out your orders. You're not deaf, are you?'

'What orders?' I asked.

'You were ordered to do what you liked. But you don't seem to know what you do like. You don't want us to give you orders about that too, do you? For goodness' sake like something!'

'I'd like to fly to North Africa.'

'Ah now, that's better. The airfield is to the east of the town, down by the sea. A hospital plane brings wounded into Catania from time to time whenever the weather's too bad between Derna and Athens. It usually flies back to Derna the same day. Is that a broad enough hint for you?'

'But I haven't got any travel papers. I won't be allowed on the plane.'

'The pilots have strict orders to tell all military personnel, of whatever rank, who ask for a lift, that the hospital plane is protected by the Geneva Convention and is not permitted to take military personnel.'

'Not even doctors?'

'You're a military doctor. That counts as military personnel.'

'So, I've no chance of a lift?'

'No military personnel may fly to die front by the hospital plane apart from the crew themselves. But the pilot has no orders to turn you out of the plane if you're already in it.'

'So, I can't have a lift, but if I take one nothing will be done to stop me. Is that military logic?'

'It takes time to get to know how it works. I can hardly wait to see if you get to Africa on the first plane.'

'Well,' I said, 'it's simple then: I ask the pilot if I can have a lift, and when he says no, I climb in and take one.'

'No, no, no,' said the Sergeant-Major. 'If you were caught over in Derna and the pilot said he'd told you that you couldn't come you'd find yourself court-martialed. If, however, he said he didn't see you, then you'd probably be given a medal for your keenness in trying to get to the front.'

'Ah, I see. So, I simply climb into the aircraft and fly with it. I won't say anything to the pilot at all.'

'That won't be so easy. The pilot doesn't just leave his machine standing around for anyone to climb into. An aircraft isn't a tram, you know.'

'But then how am I to get into it?'

'The pilot has a key to the door in the fuselage. If the door's open, then you can climb in.'

'But if I'm caught in Derna and the pilot says he let me in, then surely we'll both be court-martialed?'

'Certainly,' said the Sergeant-Major, 'I didn't say you were to ask the pilot to let you into the aircraft. You mustn't ask him. You'll be his superior officer so you must give him orders. He's only superior to you while the plane's actually in flight. When it's on the ground and the pilot is on the ground too, you're in a position to give him an order, although of course such an order mustn't contradict his instructions. But you can order him to leave the fuselage door open. The pilot would have to obey that or he'd be liable for a court martial for refusal to obey an order.'

'Well, I think I understand,' I said. 'Some of my lunatics used to be bound by fairly rigid rituals of one sort or another, but I never met anything as complicated as this before.'

The billeting officer in Catania put me in a little Pension in the Via Etna. It was the middle of November and extremely cold in my room, which had tiled walls and no heating. I don't think I was ever so cold in my life as I was in Sicily. Every morning I went to the airfield to ask what the weather was like at Athens. When I was told that the sky over Greece was cloudless, I went back to the town again. No aircraft would be expected that day.

I spent all day wandering about the town. Little blue flames spurted up from the gaps between the big lumps of lava with which the streets of Catania were paved. These originated in the yellow sulphur which is mined here and carried down in gaily coloured carts to the harbour. The road taken by these carts was marked by a thin trail of sulphur. The street urchins of Catania used to set light to this so that little blue flames were soon creeping all over the town.

On the tenth day of my stay in Sicily I heard that there was a thick layer of cloud over Greece. I went back to the town and fetched my kitbag. About midday, a hospital plane landed at Catania as expected. By contrast with the military planes, it was painted white all over. A Red Cross was painted on both sides of the fuselage and on the top and bottom of the wings. The plane was due to start off again in two hours.

The pilot was a sergeant. When he was about to climb into his machine again, I said: 'Open the door of the fuselage.' He opened it. Then he went back to the pilot's cabin. He didn't look at me. I climbed into the machine and sat down on an empty stretcher. Then the door was closed again. I waited. A few minutes later the aircraft took off.

We flew at a great height over the Mediterranean. The gigantic snow-capped mass of Etna rose clearly out of the mist which covered the sea. An hour later the African coast came into view. The mountain chain of Cyrenaica appeared to fall abruptly down to the sea and its gaily coloured rock shone in the sun. It was a picture of eternal peace. The deep blue of the Mediterranean shone like some giant flame.

Then we landed in a cloud of red dust which rose a good three hundred feet into the air. The aerodrome at Derna seemed deserted. I got out of the machine, threw my kit-bag down into the red sand and looked about me. The pilot had disappeared. The white hospital plane, my blue kitbag and I in my yellow tropical uniform were alone in a desert of red sand. Apart from us there was absolutely nothing to be seen. Not a house, not a shrub. Four fighters suddenly roared towards me thirty feet above the ground. It was a wonderful sight. The meeting of modern science with the timeless desert. I could see the heads of the pilots quite clearly. I waved to them while they were still some way off. I was in Africa, a free man. It was good to be alive.

The next moment a figure appeared out of the red dust close to where I was standing. He must have been lying in a fox-hole, completely hidden to view. He wore the uniform of a Captain of the Luftwaffe. I saluted. He said:

'What a splendid idea to wave to the British like that! They must have thought you were one of them. There are a lot of prisoners at large round here. If you hadn't waved, I'd have been picking your remains out of the dust by now. That's what I call presence of mind. Can I give you a lift in my car?'

He waved to what was apparently open desert. The next moment a red dust cloud appeared from that direction, growing larger and larger like some vast fire sweeping the desert as it approached. A few minutes later a small motor-car was standing before us.

'In you get, Doctor,' said the Captain. 'We'll go down into Derna.'

When we got to the Mess, he told his brother officers about the trick with which I had fooled the British. It was a most hospitable welcome.

Chapter 21

/\

Lieutenant Vossmenge of the medical corps spent a whole year as a medical officer on the North African front. In November 1941 he found himself in the middle of the retreat of General Rommel's army. He was transferred to a mobile hospital unit of the Luftwaffe and later took part in the advance to El Alamein. He escaped capture with the rest of the Africa Corps by being transferred to the Luftwaffe hospital in Rome. The Judge Advocate-General's Department in Rome made frequent use of him as an expert in psychiatry, in addition to which he was consulted by the staff of the General Officer Commanding the Luftwaffe in Italy on a number of problems concerning his men's psychological welfare.

'Accused, what have you to say in your defence? You have heard the sworn evidence of Lance Corporal Sachs. He maintains that you visited him in his tent after an officers' mess party in 1942 in the neighbourhood of Sabratha in North Africa. He also maintains that you made unmistakable homosexual advances to him. Accused, describe what happened on the night in question!'

The accused, a Captain in the Pay Corps called Bertram, answered as follows:

'I had undoubtedly had too much to drink and went to the wrong tent by mistake. My tent was next to Lance Corporal Sachs's. As I was trying to get into the tent, I stumbled in the darkness over one of the guy-ropes and fell onto Lance Corporal Sachs's bed. He was fast asleep. I don't know what happened after that. I must have gone to sleep at once. When I woke up towards morning, I found myself lying in Lance Corporal Sachs's bed. He was no longer there himself.'

'That is correct, accused. Lance Corporal Sachs left the tent as soon as you got into bed with him. He spent the rest of the night in your unit's kitchen.

'The next morning, he reported what had happened during the night to the officer in charge of his unit. The indictment which the prosecutor has just read out was then drawn up. Owing to the retreat of Rommel's army the trial could not take place in North Africa. The Field Marshal has allotted the case to be tried by the Judge Advocate-General's department in Rome. Accused, are you a homosexual?'

'I am not a homosexual.'

Judge Advocate Dr Magnus then rose.

'I have to inform the court,' he said to the other members of the bench, 'that in the course of interrogation the accused has consistently maintained that he was sexually normal. Besides as we have already heard, he admits that on the evening in question, on which he got into bed with Lance Corporal Sachs, he was drunk. Lance Corporal Sachs, however, stands by his evidence, according to which the accused behaved in an unmistakably homosexual manner. Here are

Lance Corporal Sachs's words: "Owing to the heat I was lying naked on my bed in the tent. I had fallen fast asleep but was woken up by the accused making homosexual advances to me and saying: Move over, darling, life is so short."'

'I can't have said that. I'm not a homosexual,' said the Pay Corps Captain.

'Accused, you are to speak only when you are asked a question. I would now like to ask the psychiatrist to give his opinion as to whether, at the time of the incident, the accused was capable of knowing that what he was doing was wrong, and, if so, whether he was in a condition to act in accordance with such knowledge, or whether perhaps his responsibility was diminished within the meaning of Section 51 Paragraph I of military regulations. Further I would like the psychiatrist to give his opinion as to whether or not the accused is homosexually inclined, and, if so, whether such homosexual inclinations are sufficiently determined by biological development to limit the accused's responsibility in such matters.'

I rose to my feet and gave my name, age, profession and rank.

'Gentlemen,' I said, 'I've known the accused personally since the days of my service on the North African front. He never struck me as being a homosexual. I admit, though, that there is not necessarily any difference, psycho-pathologically speaking, between homosexuals and those who are sexually normal. The brandy we got in North Africa was often of doubtful quality and of high alcoholic content and it made people drunk very quickly. I have often observed the accused after mess parties such as the one in question. He would talk utter nonsense when he was in this condition and be unable to recognise anyone. According to witnesses, a great deal was drunk on this particular evening in Sabratha, too. Presumably the accused drank even more than the others. Witnesses have testified that the accused was quite incapable of forming a coherent sentence by the end of the party. I therefore have no doubt that at the time of the incident the accused was in such a condition as to have no proper sense of responsibility within the meaning of Section 51 Paragraph I of military regulations.'

I sat down again.

'According to what you have just said then, the accused ought not to be prosecuted for an offence against Section 175 of military regulations but for being drunk and incapable under Section 330a. The accused's liability must be determined by an objective assessment of the facts. Objectively speaking, the accused made clear homosexual advances. Now you suggest that he is not a homosexual. Could the accused while under the influence of drink not have given expression to some homosexual urge of which he had perhaps hitherto remained unconscious?'

I said that I thought this was very improbable, but that I wasn't wholly able to exclude it.

The sentence of the court ran as follows:

'The accused is sentenced to six weeks detention for being drunk and incapable under Section 330a. In assessing the nature of the offence, the court was of the opinion that the accused, who is not in general homosexually inclined, nevertheless showed a tendency to behave in a homosexual manner while under the influence of strong alcoholic drinks.'

Afterwards I had a private conversation with Dr Magnus, the Judge Advocate at Bertram's trial.

'I always thought,' I said, 'that lawyers were primarily concerned with logic. But to-day I learnt differently. I can easily imagine what happened that night in Sabratha. There was one more party going on in the officers' mess. Towards morning this hopelessly drunk Pay Corps Captain comes reeling into Lance Corporal Sachs's tent. Now in civilian life Lance Corporal Sachs is a schoolmaster while the Pay Corps Captain is a small shopkeeper. Well, the small shopkeeper who is now an officer stumbles over the guy-ropes onto the schoolmaster's bed. The latter uses the opportunity to air his long-harboured resentment against this curious distortion of the social system. He lays information against the Pay Corps Captain to suggest that he is a homosexual. Don't you think that's probably how it was, Dr Magnus?'

'It might have been like that, Doctor, but it is now established as evidence that the man made homosexual advances and there's no getting round it.'

'But this could easily have happened to you! You might well have gone into the wrong tent by mistake and stumbled over the guy-ropes onto some Lance Corporal's bed!'

'Only I probably wouldn't have said: "Move over, darling, life is so short".'

'The Pay Corps Captain was drunk. He might easily have thought the Lance Corporal was a woman.'

'Quite possible, Doctor. And it is because he was too drunk to know what he was doing that he had to be punished.'

'But you added the taint of a homosexual tendency as well.'

'We wouldn't have been able to punish him otherwise. Drunkenness alone isn't punishable.'

'That's just where you seem to be so illogical,' I answered. 'I dare say all the officers were senselessly drunk that night. One of them, through a sheer piece of bad luck, gets suspected of making homosexual advances to someone. And so, he is punished. The others who were all equally drunk go unpunished.'

'He's only got six weeks, Doctor, and he's served that already while waiting for trial. You couldn't expect him to get away with it altogether. The others who were drunk that evening were just lucky. They didn't fall onto a Lance Corporal's bed and weren't suspected of homosexuality. I have to go on the facts as they stand, and in this case, there is no doubt that the probability of a homosexual urge of some sort has to be accepted. If you drink a glass of beer, Doctor, I have to assume that you drink it because you're thirsty. And the behaviour of the Pay Corps Captain leads me to assume some sort of homosexual urge.'

'But if I fall into a lake, what do you assume if I start swallowing water?'

'I assume that you can't swim, and that can be an offence too in certain circumstances. Besides, the case is closed now.'

But it wasn't closed. The Field Marshal refused to confirm the sentence. He returned the case to the Judge Advocate-General's department for a new trial on the grounds that he didn't want any homosexuals in his army. He wanted the Pay Corps Captain degraded.

At Bertram's second trial the Judge Advocate-General appointed a prosecutor for whom the General Officer Commanding's wishes had the force of law. I was again co-opted as psychiatric adviser. When I again expressed myself doubtful of the accused's homosexuality and again said that I thought it improbable that he could have experienced a homosexual urge while under the influence of alcohol, the prosecutor asked me if I didn't think that the accused's behaviour on that particular night had been unworthy of an officer. I replied that there was no point in entering into a discussion with him on the standards of behaviour to be expected of an officer. 'Besides,' I said, 'we're living in a period of social

160

levelling. In the course of this war, I've noticed officers' behaviour approximating more and more to that of the men.'

'How do you view the accused's behaviour from a moral point of view, then?' asked the Prosecutor.

'I'm here as a psychiatric expert,' I replied. 'The principles governing the science which I represent are the same as those governing every branch of science. Scientific evidence must be factual and susceptible to criticism. Morality and codes of behaviour are no concern of ours.'

'I wonder,' said the Prosecutor, 'if the psychiatric expert is really in a position to give useful information to the court on the subject of the accused's homosexuality. Only a person who shuns homosexuality as an unnatural vice really has any right to speak on the matter. An objective approach to homosexuality presupposes a certain sympathy with it. You, Doctor, have more than once assumed the role of counsel for the defence in the course of your evidence. I therefore ask the court to dismiss the psychiatric expert from the case on the grounds of partiality.'

The court withdrew to consider the matter. Then it returned and gave its opinion: 'The psychiatric expert is retained. He should be careful however not to give his evidence as if it were evidence for the defence. Moreover, he should do no more than answer the question put to him.'

The trial continued. I asked the court if I could make a statement and received permission to do so.

'August Bier,' I began, 'used to say that every subject could be considered from three points of view—the legal, the medical and the common sense. If we consider what the court calls the material evidence in this case we find what is, from a legal point of view, a homosexual action, but what, from the medical point of view, is not a homosexual action, for medical science knows no such thing as a homosexual action isolated from the context of the homosexual man, whose homosexual actions are conditioned by biological maladjustment or neurosis. This condition cannot suddenly develop under the influence of alcohol at two o'clock in the morning and disappear again the next day. Homosexuality can't be brought on by external influences in the same way as intoxication can be brought on by alcohol. Homosexuality embraces the whole relationship of one man with another. We doctors would never dare to draw positive conclusions about the pattern of a man's personality from a single momentary action abstracted from one short period of his life.

'I would therefore like to draw the court's attention to the clear distinction between the legal and the medical approach. At the same time, I cannot hide from the court the alarm with which we doctors view recent efforts to exclude homosexuals from the community altogether. In Hamburg and other big cities homosexuals used to be allowed to have their own clubs. There they could meet each other without having to search for suitable partners among adolescents. Whenever a club of this sort held a party to celebrate its foundation the police would be invited. The Chief of Police invariably attended, and the police thus always knew who the homosexuals were. To-day these clubs have been closed down. Homosexuals are persecuted by the law and driven back into anonymity. They know how to keep under cover too. They are no longer always recognisable even to each other. So, they're forced to look for their partners in the streets. And they look for them among the youth. Now the one danger which homosexuals do represent to the community is that they may occasionally seduce normal youths and make homosexuals of them. So, this ruthless persecution increases the homosexual danger. I should just add that from a psychological and medical point of view it is inaccurate to speak of homosexuals in general terms like this. Homosexuals can't be classified as a single homogeneous group; I must ask the court to take this into account when putting questions to me about the alleged homosexuality of the prisoner.'

But no more questions were put to me.

This time the sentence was a year's imprisonment. That was the minimum penalty involving degradation. The Field Marshal had his wish. The psychiatric expert's words had fallen on thin air.

The Pay Corps Captain shot himself in his office immediately after the trial. When I reported his death to the Judge Advocate, he said:

'What was the cause of death?'

He had obviously expected me to say, 'a bullet wound in the head'. But instead, I answered:

'His death can be attributed to three different instances of human fallibility. First, as the psychiatric expert I was unable to say with absolute certainty that the accused was not a homosexual. There is no clinical symptom by which homosexuality can be diagnosed, so in the last resort I had to leave the matter open—that is, from the point of view of what you lawyers call the material evidence. Secondly the law, which rightly recognises that an offence committed in a state of intoxication remains an offence, prescribes that the penalty for it should be in accordance with the material evidence even though the offenders state of intoxication may absolve him from a normal sense of responsibility and to some extent dissociate him from what he has done. Thus, unfortunately after the first trial the accused went on record as having homosexual tendencies. The third cause was the

Field Marshal's inability, in view of his ignorance both of the law and of medicine, to understand any of these technical complications. His attitude was that all this legal and medical talk was really based on an insufficient knowledge of what had actually happened. So, he insisted on the degradation of a perfectly good soldier whom he wrongly took to be a homosexual.

'In any case,' I said, excusing myself for the boldness of my remark, 'an Army Commander who actually wants to degrade one of his men seems to me little better than an oriental potentate enjoying the power of life and death over his subjects.'

Chapter 22

As I was on the point of leaving the Italuft building I heard a most singular noise issuing from the General's office. It was the sort of noise one usually only hears in the Zoo. A muffled roaring echoed from behind closed doors. I had been told that the General was an enthusiastic sportsman: could he have brought some stag or buffalo back to Rome to teach him tricks in his office? With some curiosity I went into his ante-room and asked his secretary the cause of these strange animal noises.

'Neither stag nor buffalo,' said the lady. 'That's the lion of Cagliari.'

The next moment there was another long-drawn-out muffled roar; then the doors flew open and the General appeared.

'I can't stand it any longer,' he cried. 'I'll have the fellow court-martialed. For cowardice in the face of the enemy. I'll have him shot.' He rushed up and down the room in a fury. At the word 'shot' the roaring noise started up inside the room again. The General turned round as if the noise was driving him mad. 'It's terrible!' he cried. 'I can't stand it!' And he rushed out into the corridor.

'Go on, Doctor,' said the General's secretary. 'You take over the madman. I'll go and talk to the General.'

On a thick carpet in front of a huge desk in the General's office lay a powerfully built man of about forty-eight in the uniform of a Colonel of the Luftwaffe. His eyes were turned up so that only the whites were showing. When I spoke to him, he looked up at me mistrustfully, then revolved on his axis a few times on the carpet, and eventually rolled away under the desk. By talking to him soothingly I managed to entice him out from tinder the desk and make him sit in one of the huge leather arm-chairs which filled the room. All at once the Colonel leapt to his feet with a muffled roar, bent his head right over backwards and fell down on the carpet again. The General had just come back into the room. With him was the Senior Medical Officer, Colonel Strube, my highest-ranking superior on the Italian front.

The General left the room again in a hurry, as the Luftwaffe Colonel once more started rolling round on the floor and roaring like a sick animal.

'Here you have an absolutely classical example of hysteria,' I said to the Senior Medical Officer. 'We psychiatrists didn't believe they existed anymore.'

'But it's unheard of,' cried the Senior Medical Officer. 'A German officer hysterical! Stand up!' he shouted at the Colonel. 'Pull yourself together!'

The Colonel writhed around on the carpet rolling his eyes. The General's secretary came forward and took the Senior Medical Officer's arm.

'Come on,' she said. 'Leave it to our soul specialist. You're only in his way.'

And she left the room with him. The women at Italuft possessed an extraordinary authority.

I went to the General's telephone and had myself put through to my hospital on the Piazza Vescovo. The Colonel lay tinder the desk making grunting noises. When the hospital answered I ordered an ambulance and two men with a stretcher and hung up again. Only the Colonel's feet were now visible. I crept under the desk, too, and tried a little mild hypnosis. I had no success at first. It was the first time I had ever tried to hypnotise someone under a General's desk. But by the time the ambulance arrived the Colonel was lying peacefully asleep on the General's sofa. My men put him on a stretcher, spread a blanket over him and carried him down the steps to the ambulance. Throughout the journey to the hospital the patient remained fast asleep. He woke up during the afternoon and asked me what had happened. I told him he'd had 'a nervous breakdown' and was badly in need of some rest.

A few days later the General sent for me. In the meantime, I'd been having a number of conversations with my patient.

'How's Colonel Wetzenstein?' the General asked me, motioning me to sit down in a heavy leather arm-chair. 'I hear you regard it as a case of hysteria?'

I said I did.

'That's not really an illness, is it?' asked the General.

'He's not suffering from any organic mental illness,' I replied, 'but hysteria is an illness all right, if not in the usual sense of the word.'

'Doctor,' said the General, 'I simply can't understand it. Colonel Wetzenstein has left his post at the front without orders and come to Rome. When I told him here in this room that I'd have him court-martialed for cowardice in the face of the enemy he started all that nonsense. You say he's ill, though not in the usual sense of the word. As a layman it looks to me as if this illness was pure imagination or else simply put on to avoid a court martial.'

'I don't wish to contradict the General,' I said, 'but I don't think the General really gets to the heart of the matter. Will the General permit me to speak openly?'

'Of course, Doctor. Forget that I'm your General. As a commander of men, I'm also a sort of father to them, I'm interested in the welfare of each one of them.'

'General, when the Colonel came to you in desperate need of help, it wasn't a very fatherly action immediately to threaten him with a court martial. What sort of father is it who turns against his son without even hearing what he has to say?'

'Colonel Wetzenstein left his post in the face of the enemy entirely without orders.'

'And why do you think the Colonel left his post, General?'

'I think he was afraid.'

'Afraid of what?'

'Of the enemy.'

'I very much doubt it. Colonel Wetzenstein won the highest decorations for bravery in the first World War. He was one of the most successful fighter pilots we had.'

'That was in 1916, Doctor. It's 1943 now.'

'Do you think a man can change as much as that in a life-time? The young Lieutenant Wetzenstein who fought dog-fights with the enemy in his rickety old machine in 1916 must certainly have known fear. Every soldier in the face of death does. But he succeeded in triumphing over it. He laid, fear aside like an old coat. Man can do that by use of his reason or will or whatever you like to call it. And man is more and more under the control of his reason as he gets older. Why should Colonel Wetzenstein of the second World War be less able to control his fear than Lieutenant Wetzenstein of the first?'

'The fellow may have become prematurely senile for all I know! You should know more about that than I do, Doctor.'

'General, you appointed Colonel Wetzenstein to an important post in charge of supplies in Sardinia. If it were true that you had appointed a senile officer to a responsible frontline post, would you continue to have faith in your judgment? Wouldn't you do better to hand over the appointment of all your commanders to a psychiatrist like me?'

'You're quite right, Doctor, if there'd been anything wrong with the Colonel, I would have noticed it. But what do you think he's afraid of?'

'Himself. Of his own inadequacy. Of the possibility of failing altogether, and of the consequences of such failure.'

'Explain yourself.'

'You've said I can speak openly, General. I shall take you at your word. You appointed Colonel Wetzenstein as officer in charge of supplies for Sardinia. May I ask what his qualifications for the job were? Did the Colonel have any experience of that sort of command?'

'Well, you certainly put me through it. But why not? All right then: I transferred Colonel Wetzenstein to a post on a quiet sector of the front at the express request of the Chief of the Air Staff. The Reichsmarshal wanted promotion for his old friend who had been a fighter-pilot with him in the first World War. But before he could be promoted, he needed a year's front-line experience. Sardinia was the quietest place I could think of, so that was where I sent him. Only I shouldn't really have told you that.'

'It's only the human side of this that interests me, General,' I said. 'I want you to understand why the Colonel suddenly became hysterical.'

'I'm very anxious to hear your opinion,' said the General. 'At this moment I think of you as a family doctor explaining the psychological development of one of my children.'

'You know what post Colonel Wetzenstein held before he was sent to Cagliari, General?'

'I think he had a job in the Air Ministry for a time. Then he was in command of a small airfield in Westphalia.'

'Where about one machine landed a year, and then only when it was lost.'

'You seem very well informed.'

'And from this airfield, where complete peace reigned, Colonel Wetzenstein was transferred to Sardinia. Hardly had he arrived there when a fighter group was also moved to Sardinia, and the peaceful island was turned into a battle ground. Its southern end was attacked by British bombers daily.

'It became more and more difficult to ensure supplies of fuel and ammunition. The tankers could no longer unload in Cagliari but had to be diverted to Olbia at the northern end of the island. From there the fuel had to be brought southwards by single track railway. Right across the island, providing an ideal target for partisans.'

'Which they took full advantage of. But what has this got to do with our problem child?'

'Colonel Wetzenstein found himself suddenly faced by a situation he couldn't deal with. Listen to the details of his career to date: scraped his matriculation at the age of seventeen. Trained as a fighter pilot. After the war, apprenticed in business for a time. Then a confidential clerk. Finally, director of a vacuum cleaner factory. In 1937 he returned to the active list, at the Reichsmarshal's insistence. Head of a personnel section at the Air Ministry. Then given command of an airfield where there was no flying. Then put in charge of supplies in Sardinia. A vital sector. You might as well have put me in charge of supplies there, General. I would at least have known what Otto fuel was.'

'Do you mean to say Colonel Wetzenstein didn't know what Otto fuel was?'

'Certainly. When the bombing of Cagliari started Colonel Wetzenstein began to realise that he wasn't up to the job. Sometimes he managed to conceal his inexperience, although he knew quite well that his technical ignorance was already proving a disadvantage to his men. He sent you a radio message asking to be relieved of his post.'

'And I refused. I had no idea what was going on.'

'His feeling of insecurity increased daily. The fighter squadrons were ordered into action, but they couldn't take off because they had no petrol. The commander of the fighter group wouldn't leave Colonel Wetzenstein alone. He was determined to get his petrol. Colonel Wetzenstein rang up Olbia in his presence to ask where the petrol was. He was told that two thousand litres of Otto were on the way. He put the receiver down and asked the commander of the fighter group who Otto was. He had never heard of such a thing. How could he have heard of it, General? No one had ever told him. Now I'd like to put a rather disrespectful question to you, General.'

'You can't be more disrespectful than you've been already. Still, go on!'

'If you were suffering from acute appendicitis, General, and asked me who should operate on you, and I recommended the Senior Medical Officer, Colonel Strube, what would you think of me?'

'For God's sake, a doctor who's nothing more than a pen-pusher! He'd kill me.'

'And who would be responsible for your death?'

'I see what you're getting at. So, I'm really responsible for Colonel Wetzenstein's failure? I should never have entrusted him with a post for which he had no training?'

'That's not for me to say, General. I was really getting at something else. Let us assume now that Colonel Strube, whom you call a pen-pusher, were ordered to operate on your appendix. Colonel Strube isn't a surgeon. He's never operated on anyone in his life. Would you think him particularly competent if, instead of saying that he was quite unqualified to carry out the order, he obeyed it?'

'So, you mean Colonel Wetzenstein left his post in Cagliari from a higher sense of duty?'

'He asked you to relieve him. You refused. He couldn't explain his reasons for wanting to be relieved in a radio message. He had to come and see you personally. He trusted to your humanity and your understanding. So, he got into his aircraft and flew to Rome. He wanted to turn to you in confidence, to explain the difficulty he was in and talk to you like a father. He wanted to tell you that it was a mistake to put him in command of supplies. He didn't have the necessary experience and he was making a terrible mess of it. This was what he wanted to say to you. He flew to Rome, reported to you and what did you do, General?'

'I roared at him and told him I'd have him court-martialed for cowardice in the face of the enemy.'

'And Colonel Wetszenstein replied with an attack of hysteria.'

'But at least this shows he must be a hysteric. We can't have people like that in our command.'

'Hysteria isn't nearly so contemptible as you seem to think, General,' I said. 'We're all capable of reacting hysterically in certain circumstances. Put yourself in the wretched man's position. He was heading for disaster in Cagliari. What was he to do? Wasn't it better to turn to his General for advice? You were the only man who could save the situation. But before he could start explaining things, you reproached him with cowardice in the face of the enemy. Every way out seemed blocked. So, he took refuge in illness. But he didn't do this simply to get his head out of the noose. It happened half mechanically. Man isn't meant to sacrifice himself senselessly and suffer a shameful death without cause. Colonel Wetzenstein had proved on the Western Front in the first World War that he was ready to sacrifice his life for an ideal. He wouldn't have been afraid of an honourable death in Cagliari either. But when an irreproachable family man with a respectable position in civilian life, who is now a staff officer, suddenly finds himself unjustly charged with cowardice, then a part of his personality revolts. The air battles of 1916, the struggle for a position in civilian life after the war, the daily resolve always to remain a man of honour—all were suddenly in vain. He had left his post without orders, and his General, in whom he had complete confidence and who was the only man who could help him, called him a coward and wanted to court-martial him.'

'And what do you think should be done, Doctor?'

'If you do court-martial him, General, I shall be asked in my role as psychiatric expert if I think the accused was in full possession of his faculties at the time of the alleged offence. What am I to say? Colonel Wetzenstein's will no longer existed when he collapsed here in this room. But the court martial isn't interested in what happened here in this room. The material evidence is that he left Cagliari without orders, and that's all that's relevant. And that happened before his fit of hysteria. In Cagliari the Colonel was unquestionably in full command of his will and all his other faculties. The court martial would therefore have to find him guilty. You would be one good officer the less, General. But what does that matter? We've plenty of officers to take his place. Discipline must be maintained at all costs.'

'I must say that when I think of Colonel Strube operating on me simply because he's been ordered to do so, I begin to see a refusal to obey an order in a different light altogether.'

The General fell silent for a moment. Then he went on:

'Right, Doctor, I've changed my mind. I'll relieve Colonel Wetzenstein of his post at once on account of illness. You make out the medical report. But don't put in the word hysteria. German Colonels don't have hysteria. Haven't you got some other Greek name you could use?'

'General,' I said, 'Since it's a question of preventing an injustice I shall avoid the Greek name of the illness altogether.'

The General gave a cynical laugh and dismissed me.

Chapter 23

Our hospital was situated in a multi-storeyed block of flats in the Piazza Vescovo. It had originally been intended only for the staff personnel stationed in Rome and for troops in transit. But as the front gradually crept nearer, numerous Luftwaffe units were transferred to Central Italy. The hospital in Rome became too small. Every effort of the doctor in charge, Major Müller, to enlarge the hospital foundered on the militant patriotism of the Senior Medical Officer, Colonel Strube. He described Major Müller's view that Rome might well be bombed one day as a typical piece of civilian defeatism and forbade him to look around for a more suitable site for a hospital. In June 1943 British bombers attacked the airfield at Grosseto, north of Rome. Our hospital was already full to overflowing. The Field Marshal himself had just paid us a visit and deplored the fact that in order to get to die wards he had to step over a number of badly wounded men lying in the corridors. And now a hospital train arrived in Rome from Grosseto.

I was at a conference in our head doctor's office when an urgent call for Major Müller came through from Colonel Strube. The Senior Medical Officer announced that forty badly wounded men would be arriving at the hospital that day.

'And where are we to put them?' asked Major Müller. 'The hospital is overflowing as it is. I can't tie another man.'

'You'll take the lot!' shouted Colonel Strube down the telephone. 'How you do so is your own affair!'

'I respectfully beg to inform the Colonel that our hospital is quite unfitted for emergencies of this kind,' said Major Müller. 'I warned the Colonel of this some time back, but the Colonel chose to disregard my warnings as unduly pessimistic. Now that the emergency has arisen, I beg the Colonel to accept responsibility for the wounded from Grosseto himself.'

'No excuses, Müller,' shouted Strube, 'The responsibility for these wounded is yours and no one else's.'

'I can't take them. There's no more room. We've got men lying in the corridors and on the stairs here as it is.'

'I don't care about that. This is a categorical order to take them in. I hope you're clear about the consequences of refusing to obey an order. That's all.' He rang off.

'That's it. Order the impossible, that's how to get away with being a senior officer!' Major Müller hurled the receiver to the ground, threw an ash-tray at the wall and splintered a pen from his desk between two fingers. Then he calmed down, laid his right arm on my shoulder and said:

'Vossmenge, can't you get rid of this troublesome Colonel for me? Come on, you know how to deal with lunatics, don't you? Well, get rid of him for me. I don't want to see him again.'

'Give me four days,' I said.

'All right,' sighed Müller. 'I suppose we can wait that long.'

Here I should mention that a year before, when we had been together with a Luftwaffe mobile hospital unit in North Africa, Major Müller had probably saved my life. I was to have been court-martialed for saying in a letter home that the senior officers in the Medical Corps were neither proper doctors nor proper soldiers and that for them the campaign was more in the nature of a commercial foray than a measure for the defence of the Fatherland. Just before I sent this letter off, a hospital plane flying between Tripoli and Germany had crashed in the Alps and disintegrated. It had been overloaded, but not with wounded. It was chock full of coffee, olive oil and carpets, all of which had been bought by our senior officers for their families in the bazaars. This letter of mine was sent to the Air Ministry. It was clear that my mail was being censored. The Senior Medical Officer of the Luftwaffe Southern Command came down to collect the summary of evidence against me. I was to be court-martialed for bringing the Wehrmacht into contempt. Whereupon Major Müller, then deputy head of our hospital in Apollonia, which was our base at the time, made it clear that he would get all his colleagues in North Africa to sign a declaration stating that my criticisms had been perfectly justified. If it was a scandal the Senior Medical Officer wanted, all he had to do was to go ahead with the summary of evidence against me. Every doctor in the North African theatre of war would soon be up before a court martial. There would be a lot of fun.

The Senior Medical Officer of Southern Command went away again, and I never heard anything more about the summary of evidence.

Ever since then I had had a feeling of gratitude for Major Müller and had made a point of trying to comply with his every wish. Now he expressed the wish to be rid of this maddening Colonel.

I went to see the General the same day. His secretary had told me that my psychology lesson in the case of Colonel Wetzenstein had made a good impression.

'Well, Doctor?' said the General, offering me a cigarette. 'What about becoming psychiatric consultant to the General Officer Commanding the Luftwaffe in Italy?'

'Might I respectfully ask the General whether in such a position I could draw his attention to certain peculiarities among his own staff?'

'Why not? I was able to see recently that even a General has something to learn from a psychiatrist.'

'And would such psychiatric advice be confined only to those members of the staff who were lower than me in rank, or could it be also extended to senior officers?'

'There would be no distinction between the two,' said the General. 'You're not issuing orders, but simply giving me advice as a specialist. You are therefore at liberty to report on your superiors.'

'Then I respectfully beg to inform the General of the first case of serious mental disturbance on his staff.'

'You don't waste much time, Doctor. Wait a minute, let me guess! Do you mean Colonel von Fetwys? I think there's a screw loose there somewhere.'

'No, General, I mean Colonel Strube.'

'Well, well! You don't mean that seriously, Doctor, do you? I thought you doctors stuck together through thick and thin. How long has Colonel Strube been off his head?'

'He isn't off his head in the ordinary sense of the phrase.

May I explain, General?'

'Please do.'

'The General may be aware that the Luftwaffe was formed in something of a hurry in 1935.'

'A hurry is an understatement, Doctor. But go on.'

'A number of doctors were needed to organise the medical corps.'

'Yes, I know that. Go on.'

'In 1935 doctors were doing very well in Germany. If a doctor with a medium-sized practice went into the Luftwaffe it meant giving up the greater part of his income, for the Luftwaffe didn't pay much. Apart from which a good doctor will hang on to the actual practice of his profession for all he's worth. The organisation of a medical corps whose chief eventual concern will be the examination of a lot of young men who are perfectly fit is no job for any doctor. Have you ever heard of a doctor voluntarily giving up his profession because he didn't like it?'

'You're trying to suggest that those doctors who volunteered for the Luftwaffe weren't exactly the best, is that it, Doctor?'

'There were undoubtedly a number of idealists among them, General,' I said. 'But there were also a lot who hoped to earn more in the Luftwaffe than they could ever expect from their civilian practices. Their practices can't therefore have been up to much. So long as there isn't a surplus of doctors—and in 1935 there weren't all that number of doctors in Germany—a good doctor has no need to turn himself into a poorly paid pen-pusher.'

'So, in 1935 the Luftwaffe filled its ranks with a lot of rotten doctors. That's what you mean, is it, Doctor?'

'You exaggerate, General, but perhaps there were some rotten ones amongst them.'

'Let us assume there were. Was old Strube one of them?'

'That I don't know, General. But certainly, most of his subordinates feel that he doesn't know much about medicine. Before being called back to service he's said to have had a little village practice somewhere or other, treating the peasants with colt's foot and henbane.'

'Now it's you who are exaggerating, my dear fellow. You must have known old Strube in North Africa, didn't you?'

'The Colonel was in charge of general hygiene for the troops in those days. He tried to ban dysentery, for instance.'

'I don't believe it,' said the General. 'How did he hope to do that? Did he succeed?'

'Colonel Strube's first act was to issue an order saying that every man found with amoeba in his stool should be declared unfit for tropical service and sent home, so that the dysentery could be cured there.'

'That sounds reasonable enough.'

'Unfortunately, we found that almost every patient brought into the hospital had amoeba in his stool.'

'And you doctors sent them all home?'

'We obeyed orders for a time. But when some units were sent home to hospital almost *en bloc*, the high command rightly concluded that such precautions would soon undermine the entire fighting strength of our forces in North Africa.'

'Ah, yes,' said the General. 'I remember now. Some unit commanders, old Major Hartlaub for example, wanted to do away with doctors altogether after that. The moment the doctor appears, everyone falls ill, I remember him saying to me when I went to Benghazi. Well, how did Strube get out of that?'

'He put a ban on dysentery.'

'What do you mean? You can't ban a disease!'

'Colonel Strube tried to. He issued an order forbidding us to diagnose dysentery.'

'But that's absurd. And what did you do?'

'We didn't take any notice. Anyway, we were bound by our Hippocratic oath.'

'Your what? Oh well, go on. How does the story end?'

'Two days later the order was rescinded.'

'So, dysentery was permitted again.'

'He was advised also to rescind the first order by which all those found with amoeba in their stools were sent home.'

'And what happened to the patients?'

'The patients—that is to say those who not only had amoeba in their stools but were also clinically ill with dysentery—were sent to hospitals at the rear.'

'And the others, who had amoeba in their stools and weren't clinically ill? Didn't they get the disease?'

'No, it turned out that almost everyone who had spent a certain amount of time in North Africa had amoeba in their stools. Only a fraction of them became clinically ill with dysentery.'

'And didn't anyone know that before? Was it the campaign in North Africa that first taught us that?'

'It had been known for ages. Not by the Air Ministry of course. But there was an Austrian doctor, born in Bolzano, living in Tripoli. He had had twenty years' experience of the diseases of the country. Dr Stefanelli was his name. He had been personal doctor to Count Volpi and Marshal Balbo, the last two Governors of Tripoli. He knew all about the peculiarities of dysentery in Libya.'

'And why didn't someone consult him?'

'They didn't have a chance to. When Dr Stefanelli offered to put his special knowledge at the disposal of the Wehrmacht he was immediately sent off to Germany to get some military training. Then he was sent to the military academy.'

'And then?' asked the General.

'Then he was posted to Norway.'

'Now I know why we lost the war in North Africa,' said the General dropping heavily into a deep arm-chair.

'Quite apart from that, Colonel Strube has never recovered from the rebuff. From that day to this, if he hears anyone laughing, he thinks they're laughing at him.'

'Is it dangerous do you think?' asked the General.

'In certain circumstances, yes, General,' I said. 'He feels insecure with his subordinates and has developed a strong inferiority complex as a result. This forces him to try and assert himself. He often issues orders simply for the sake of issuing them. Colonel Strube will often transfer a hardworking doctor from one hospital, where he's badly needed, to some out of the way headquarters where his great experience is utterly wasted, simply for the sake of asserting himself over the doctor in question who may have been a high school professor in civilian life. I regard such behaviour as a symptom of mental illness, and, viewed from the standpoint of the well-being of the service as a whole, undoubtedly dangerous.'

'You may well be right, Doctor,' said the General thoughtfully. 'I must confess I've never thought much of the fellow. I'll relieve him of his post immediately. Bring me a medical report in two hours' time giving a clear and concise analysis of the case. No one else will see it apart from myself and the Chief of Staff. Understand?'

'Very good, General.'

'Thank you.' The General waved me away. 'There's only one thing, Doctor: if one day you come to the conclusion that I'm a hopeless old dodderer who's no more use to anyone,

182

will you come to me first, or go straight to the Field Marshal?'

'The war won't last that long, General.'

'Let's hope not. But what a confounded war it is. Believe me, I'd much rather be Mayor of Pöcking than a General in Rome. But what can one do about it?'

Four days later there was a new Senior Medical Officer at Italuft. I went to report to Major Müller.

'I've carried out your orders, sir. Colonel Strube won't be troubling you anymore.'

'Thank you. Stand easy. What did you do with him, throw him in the Tiber?'

'No, Major, I had him certified.'

'Quite right, my boy. God knows he was mad enough. What was your diagnosis?'

'I'm afraid that's a medical secret,' I said looking up at a medical orderly corporal who had just come into the room.

'Then whisper it to me. I don't understand that psychiatric jargon of yours anyway.'

'Hypersensitive delusions of status originating in a deficiency of the proportional faculty.'

'There you are,' said Major Müller, 'I can't make head or tail of it. It's a secret language all of its own.'

'As a surgeon you don't need to know about psychiatry,' I said. 'On the whole you simply cut away what you don't want. But you can't cut away more than two thirds of the brain or it becomes noticeable.'

'One thing I do understand even if I am a surgeon, and that is that you psychiatrists are a damned dangerous lot. One needs to be careful with you. Where's it going to end if you start getting rid of your superior officers like this?'

'But you begged me to get rid of him for you, Major.'

'Good God, Vossmenge, I didn't mean it seriously.'

'Shall I get the troublesome fellow back for you again, sir?'

'Let's wait and see what the new one's like first,' said Major Müller. 'If he doesn't suit me, I'll let you know. Thank you.'

Chapter 24

It wasn't long before Colonel von Fetwys came to consult me. He stormed into the room just as another doctor and I were busy trying to get one of the girls who worked at staff headquarters back into some sort of shape. She had drunk herself into a coma on the occasion of her proxy marriage to a Sergeant in Narvik a few days before.

'You're the nerve specialist, aren't you?' Colonel von Fetwys asked me, and when I said I was: 'Can you do anything for impotence?'

'That depends on what it's caused by, Colonel,' I answered. 'How old are you?'

'Don't be a fool, man, it's not me that's impotent. It's my son. Can you cure him or not?'

'Perhaps the Colonel would introduce me to his son?' I said politely.

The Colonel went over to the door and called in his son,

who had been waiting outside.

'This is my son,' he said. 'He's impotent. Haven't you any tablets or something like that you can give him?'

The son wore the uniform of a Lieutenant in the Luftwaffe. He was a pilot, and his neck and chest were covered with every sort of medal, including the Knight's Cross.

After we had introduced ourselves, I said in some embarrassment: 'So you're impotent. Is it a wound?'

'I thought I'd told you that. My son's impotent. Now kindly write him out a prescription of some sort—tablets or something like that. I haven't got much time.'

'So, you wish to consult me, Lieutenant,' I asked. 'I assume you're of legal age.'

'I'm just twenty,' said the Lieutenant.

'Is that part of the examination?' cried the Colonel. 'Asking him whether he's of legal age or not? Are you a nerve specialist, or aren't you?'

That was enough for me. I flung the door open and said: 'Colonel, you will kindly wait outside and stay there until I call you.'

'I am Colonel von Fetwys, the General's right-hand man. You can't order me about like that.'

'You're wrong there, Colonel,' I said, raising my voice. 'No one but the doctor has any authority in this consulting room. Now kindly go outside!'

The Colonel looked at me in astonishment. His son smiled. Then the old man said:

'All right, I'll wait outside.'

And he left the room.

The holder of the Knight's Cross sat down and stared into a corner in some embarrassment.

I said,

'Are you really impotent, or is that just what your father says?'

'My father says I am.'

'And what do you think?'

'He may be right.'

'Have you been wounded?' I asked.

'Four times.'

'Do you mind if I examine you? Undress behind the screen, please.'

I examined him. Among other wounds he had a deep scar on his thigh large enough to lay a length of rope in. But his organs were undamaged.

'Why do you, or your 'father, think you're impotent?' I asked, when the Lieutenant had dressed again. 'It's nothing to do with your wounds.'

'I told my father that.'

'And what made him suppose that you were impotent?'

'My father had an illegitimate son by the time he was my age.'

'And just because you haven't got an illegitimate son your father thinks you're impotent, is that it?'

'When I came home on leave recently, my father asked me if I was still a virgin. I said I was. Then he said to me: "Good God, man, haven't you got any brothels in North Africa?" I told him that we had once been allotted some girls from Greece, but they had hardly arrived before our airfield was shot up by fighters and some of our tents were hit. Two of the girls were killed and the others insisted on being taken back to Athens at once. Father was furious.'

'What was he furious about?'

'Our putting up a brothel in the immediate neighbourhood of the airfield. He said it was against the Geneva Convention.'

'He sounds a bit confused there,' I said. 'But what I can't see is why your father should think you're impotent just because your unit has this unfortunate accident with its girls from Greece.'

'My father simply meant that if the welfare arrangements for the troops in North Africa had been more competently organised I wouldn't still be a virgin.'

'That's a matter of opinion,' I said. 'But in any case, there's no reason to suppose that you're impotent. You haven't had a chance to prove yourself a man yet, that's all.'

'Yes, Doctor, I have. It's just that that worries my father so much.'

'My dear Lieutenant, your father seems to me to have rather peculiar views about a young man's first experience with a woman. From what you say I can guess that he used his paternal authority to send you to a brothel here in Rome. Being an obedient son, you went and found yourself repelled by the standard practices of such places. If that's impotence, Lieutenant, it does you credit for it shows that your attitude to sex is a thoroughly healthy one. I'm very glad to have met you. Please call your father in again.'

Colonel Fetwys came striding back into the room.

'Well,' he shouted while he was still outside, 'is my boy impotent? And what can you do for him?'

'I assume, Colonel,' I said, 'that your son told you in detail about his unsatisfactory visit to a brothel, and that you've therefore concluded that he's impotent.'

'When I was his age, my dear Doctor,' said the Colonel, 'I'd already had hundreds of girls. These young fellows to-day. . .'

'How many enemy machines have you shot down?' I asked Lieutenant von Fetwys.

'Seventeen, Doctor.'

'You see, Colonel, the youth of to-day have other things to worry about. When you were still barely an adult you were making conquests among the girls and counting your score. Your son shoots down enemy aircraft and counts their score. *C'est la petite différence.*'

Chapter 25

The 19th of July 1943 was a Monday. A sweltering heat lay over the hills of Rome. Punctually at ten o'clock I reported to the new Senior Medical Officer in the staff headquarters of Italuft in the Via Borelli. At the same moment a thousand enemy bombers crossed the coast on their way to attack Rome for the first time.

While the Chief was explaining to me that I had been appointed psychiatric adviser to the General Officer Commanding the Luftwaffe in Italy and transferred to the staff with the rank of Major, I myself was more intent on the familiar echoing drone of swarms of approaching four-engined bombers. The new Colonel found it difficult to conceal his impatience with me. Here was a subordinate who seemed to attach no importance at all to the honour implied by his promotion to the staff. Instead of looking his senior officer in the eye, he preferred to fix his attention on something outside the window. When I even went so far as to interrupt him by saying: 'Don't you think we ought to go to an air raid shelter?' he was unable to contain himself any longer.

'Have you no interest in what I'm telling you, then?'

'I can hear large numbers of four-engined bombers heading straight for us,' I said. 'I've had some experience of these things.'

'Nonsense,' said the Colonel. 'They'll never bomb Rome. Do you think the British would dare destroy the Vatican? The seat of a neutral sovereign state? Or St. Peter's?'

'Perhaps they won't attack the Vatican,' I said. 'But it seems to me that Italuft might be a worthwhile target.'

'A few hundred yards away from here is one of the oldest churches in Christendom. World opinion would never forgive the British if they started destroying the finest treasures of our civilisation. In my opinion,' went on the Colonel, 'we're safer here than in Abraham's bosom itself.'

Meanwhile the sound of enemy aircraft had grown appreciably louder.

'Don't you think we ought at least to send the women to the shelter?' I asked, pointing to the ante-room where the Colonel's secretary was working calmly away at her typewriter.

'You're not windy, are you?' asked the Colonel, and went on to initiate me into the duties of my new post.

In defiance of all regulation military procedure, I stood up and went over to the window. The Colonel followed me. We looked out past the university to the peaceful city slumbering in the heat. There wasn't a sign of life in the streets.

'You needn't worry,' said the Colonel. 'We know from intercepted radio messages that the British have promised the King of Italy that they won't bomb Rome.'

A rushing screaming sound now became audible. It was all too familiar to me.

'You can't attach much importance to promises like that these days, Colonel,' I said. 'Can't you hear those bombs? They're not for us. You won't hear the ones meant for us until they burst in the room.'

The Colonel looked at me in terror.

'Do you think it's possible they'd dare to bomb Rome?' he asked.

There was no need to answer. The twelve-storey building began to rock. A dull rumbling sound came rolling along the ground towards us. Huge clouds of smoke rose up in the southern part of the city. A hubbub of voices broke out from every room. Everyone rushed into the corridors.

'What is it?' cried the Colonel's secretary looking up from her work.

'The destruction of Rome,' I shouted through the din.

The first bombs were falling outside in the street. They seemed destined for us personally.

Then I was staring death in the face and I could only laugh. How little solemnity there is about the moment in which this magnificent life of ours comes to an end! A girl was screaming hysterically. It was the same girl who a short time before had assured me, when I had asked her if she had to go on working through an air-raid warning: 'We haven't time to run to the shelter every time the warning goes.' She now rushed from the room in panic but returned a moment later to fetch her handbag before hurling herself once more into the scrum of terrified human beings trying to fight their way down the far too narrow staircase.

A staff officer who had completely lost his head was running round his office in his shirt sleeves trying to find his tunic. He wanted to be properly dressed when he presented himself at the gates of hell. He couldn't get his arms into the sleeves. I gave him a hand, shouting into his ear as I did so: 'Our last hour has come! We'll never get out of here alive!' Our last hour indeed! What a third-rate expression to use in such a moment!

It was like night outside. The whole building was wrapped in a great cloud of black smoke. The electric light no longer worked. Dust and smoke poured into the room through the open window. I pressed a handkerchief to my mouth and felt my way down the stairs.

Staff officers, orderly corporals and typists were all crowded together in the cellar. They hadn't been able to reach the roomy air-raid shelter. The first bold man to try and leave the building—which everyone felt sure would soon collapse on top of us—had been killed by a bomb splinter in the street. Only ten men out of the entire headquarters staff managed to comply with regulations and reach the shelter.

It was in this attack that the southern suburbs of Rome, which lay on both sides of the road leading to the main station, were destroyed. Some bombs fell on the old cemetery of Campo Santo and ripped open the church of San Lorenzo and the graves of the Pope's parents. One stick of bombs reached as far as the Via Borelli. The street in front of the headquarters building looked like a moon landscape. But the building itself remained untouched. The craters lay all round it. Bombs had also fallen on the air-raid shelter. They had crashed through the thin roof and killed everyone inside it. There were ten fatal casualties among the staff—the ten men who had obeyed regulations and gone to the air-raid shelter. Everyone else escaped, thanks to their undisciplined behaviour; they owed their lives entirely to their own carelessness.

A week after that 19th of July on which the British broke their promise not to bomb Rome, the city was suddenly seized by a wild wave of enthusiasm. The King had thrown over Mussolini. On the day of the Dictator's arrest people went through the streets singing: *'Il carnevale e finite!'* Strips of paper from torn-up photographs of Mussolini fluttered out of the windows into the streets. Bronze busts of the Duce's head were dragged along the pavements. The emblems of Fascism—the lictors' bundles—were removed from every house. In the heart of the city someone climbed up onto a pedestal and gave an imitation of the hated dictator: he put both hands on his hips, stuck out his chin and shouted:

'Italiani! Fascisti! Il Vesuvio e fatto da me!'

(Italians! Fascists! Vesuvius was *my* achievement!)

In the public squares and gardens of the city there had been notices explaining to visitors that vegetables were now being planted in the beds instead of flowers. On these notices the words *'Orto diguerra'* (War-time allotments) had been changed to *'Torto di guerra'* (War is wrong).

Surprisingly the Italians showed no open hostility to us Germans. They looked at us mistrustfully and went about their business. But it was rather as if they were waiting for a signal to throw us into the Tiber. Unfortunately, an order appeared making the wearing of uniform compulsory, which didn't make things easier.

On the second day of Rome's celebration of her release from Fascism, when bands of determined looking youths were still storming through the streets removing the last signs of the fallen regime's authority, I travelled through the city by bus. Suddenly we were held up by a gang of young men who might have been ruffians from the Abruzzi. They gesticulated wildly at me, as apparently the only German soldier in sight, drew their knives and rushed at me yelling wildly. I was terrified. I had been warned not to go into the inner part of the city unarmed. Now I regretted my rashness as it looked as if I was about to be murdered in broad daylight. But I was not the object of the Abruzzi ruffians' attention. The city's coat-of-arms was painted on the outside of the bus at the same height as my seat. This contained a lictor's bundle that was as yet undamaged, and they hurriedly scratched it off with their knives. When they had done this, all the bystanders cheered lustily.

Chapter 26

I was now at the height of my military career: I was the General's psychiatric consultant and could move about as I liked. One of my tasks was to inspect those Luftwaffe hospitals which possessed mental departments. Most of them didn't possess one.

I met Field Marshal Kesselring in the hospital at G. and accidentally addressed him as 'Herr Feldwebel'* instead of 'Herr Feldmarschall'. But he accepted the fact that one couldn't expect a psychiatrist to distinguish between different ranks. 'So long as you leave me my salary,' said Kesselring, 'you can go on calling me "Herr Feldwebel".'

I was in Verona on the 8th of September when the news came through that Italy had opted to leave the sinking ship.

---

* Sergeant

A whole Italian Army lay ready round Verona to help shorten the war. They were to block the Alpine passes and stop reinforcements getting through to us on the Italian peninsula. But the Italians were sick of war. Perhaps too the individual Italian soldier had some misgiving about fighting against men who had been his allies only twenty-four hours before. Is it really possible at this stage of the twentieth century to say to a man: 'This is your enemy. Take your gun and kill him'? For whatever reasons, the Italians made no use of their numerical superiority, and let themselves be taken prisoner willingly enough. There was only a little local resistance here and there. It was enough, however, to bring my tourist's existence to an end for the time being, and I was allotted as medical officer to an active service battalion hastily collected from men on leave.

I had so many duties in my new role that I hardly ever got to bed. The officers in our battalion knew nothing of Italy and couldn't speak a word of the language. Most of them were on leave from the Russian front and brought some pretty crude customs with them into Italy. They used me as interpreter, guide, wine merchant, de-louser and even occasionally doctor.

We had occupied the Italian barracks in the Via del Fante, Verona, and acquired an enormous store of wine. While the men, out of an instinct for cleanliness, started scrubbing and sweeping out the barracks, the officers got to work on the wine. The ricciotto di Valpolicella was a strong dark-red wine. As we sat in the Mess a young Lieutenant, who had seen his share of danger on the Russian front, suggested the following jolly game: on a wooden shelf behind us would be set a row of schnaps glasses, which we were to try and hide with our heads from our opponents on the other side of the table. Those opposite were to do the same. Then we would draw our pistols and try to hit the schnaps glasses whenever our opponent moved his head slightly to one side or the other. The schnaps glass would only be visible for a second or two and it was in this second that one had to fire. One mustn't hit the other man's head. If one did, one lost the game and had to pay a lira into the pool.

I didn't like the idea of this game. Perhaps I hadn't drunk enough Valpolicella. I suggested an alternative. Instead of shooting here in the room, we should have a proper shooting match out on the barrack square, with targets, markers and a barrel of wine for the first prize.

While I was still busy arranging about the barrel of wine, my comrades had already begun firing on the barrack square. I was the last to shoot. I didn't really want to take part myself for I hadn't fired my pistol once during the whole war. I secretly hoped that it might have rusted up. But I couldn't be a spoil-sport. There was nothing for it but to fire. My comrades stood round me to see that I did everything properly. I saw an empty tin standing in some rubble about twenty yards ahead. Taking this for the target, I aimed carefully and fired. The tin didn't move, nor did I see any rubble spurt up. I was just about to explain to my comrades that I hadn't really meant my pistol to go off when they began to hail me as the finest shot in the battalion and awarded me the barrel of wine. It turned out that I had fired high and accidentally hit a little target standing in the furthest corner of die square which I hadn't seen at all. So, I was proclaimed champion and won considerable respect all round.

I used this new-won respect to try and ease the lot of the Italian prisoners a little. Many of the Italians hadn't been home for seven years. At last, the war appeared to be over for them. Then along came the Germans and shut them up. No Italian soldier was allowed out into the streets of Verona unless he wore a Red Cross arm-band to show that he was a medical orderly. I was given the job of distributing these arm-bands. But I hadn't been told how to discover whether those Italians who applied for arm-bands were really medical orderlies or not. It wasn't until I had given out about two thousand that I was struck by the large number of medical orderlies in the Italian army. However, I knew too little about the composition of European armies to be justified in stopping the issue on my own initiative. Finally, I gave up trying to count the number of arm-bands I had given out. Every Italian who applied got his arm-band, and, though it was obvious that a lot of them were not orderlies at all, it went against my sense of justice to treat those who had had to wait a long time for their arm-bands any differently from those who had got theirs at the very beginning.

By the afternoon I had no more arm-bands left. A remarkable sight met my eyes when I went into the town. Regiments of medical orderlies were standing about in little groups all over the place. It looked as if it had been raining medical orderlies. Soon afterwards I was sent for by the battalion commander:

'It's very strange, Doctor,' he said. 'How do you account for the fact that all the medical orderlies in the world appear to be in Verona at the moment?'

And he looked at me as if he would have liked to take a shot at a schnaps glass just behind my head. But I was lucky. I remembered what the Sergeant had told me in the Luftwaffe hospital at Catania: it's the literal wording of an order that counts in the army, regardless of whether it makes sense or not. A good soldier doesn't ask the point of an order. He obeys it, and that's all there is to it.

So, I produced my written orders which ran as follows:

'In order to safeguard the medical welfare of the prisoners Major Dr. Vossmenge is immediately to issue Red Cross arm-bands to members of the former Italian army.'

And that was what I had done.

'How many arm-bands have you given out then?' asked the battalion commander.

'I didn't count,' I said. 'But certainly not more than ten thousand.'

Chapter 27

In May 1944 I was posted to Milan. I would gladly have left the town again at once. There was a ghostly atmosphere about the place. Whole areas of the town had been completely burnt out, but the facades of the palaces were still intact. Among the ruins life pulsated as fiercely as in peacetime.

I was taken out by motor transport to Gallarate. The court martial was sitting at a place just outside it called Cardano. The Judge Advocate, Dr Hermann, a lawyer in civilian life, had set up his offices in a little country house almost entirely covered with roses. He was not one of those who stuck rigidly to the letter of the law but was very conscious of the psychological aspects of a case. He never delivered a judgment without scrupulously trying to fathom out the motives in the offender's mind. I went to see him when the day's work was over, bringing with me some salami and a bottle of chianti. There seemed to be something on his mind. I was just thinking that it would be better for me to leave again when he suddenly asked me:

'Is it possible for someone, between two attacks of malaria, to do or say something which is completely foreign to his personality?'

'How can you say what is or is not foreign to a man's personality? Personality isn't a fixture. It's changing all the time. To decide at any given moment whether the change is for better or worse is often only possible after a tedious psychiatric examination.'

'Can malaria affect the development of personality?' asked Dr Hermann.

'So long as a man's personality remains capable of development all experience will affect him one way or another, particularly illness. So why not malaria? But a deterioration in personality, in a clinical sense, can't be brought on by malaria.'

'Not even temporarily? Some sort of exceptional psychological state of mind?'

'The patient may lapse into delirium in the course of his fever,' I continued, 'but a malaria patient is always quite normal between attacks of fever.'

'Another death sentence then!' said Dr Herman. 'How I used to love my profession! And how I loathe it to-day! I've become no better than a butcher. There's blood on my hands. Almost every day a death sentence! I think I'd better make an end of it all.'

The Judge Advocate jumped up excitedly and went into his room. I followed him. He had flung himself down on the bed. I sat down beside him and waited. After a little while he turned to me and looked at me desperately. Simply to break the painful silence I said:

'If you're determined at all costs to save someone's life, then let him off.'

'How can I let a man off when all the evidence shows that he is guilty of what the court regards as a crime? I can't just decide these matters how I want to. I'm bound by the law. The Judge Advocate-General examines every case afterwards. If I were to let someone off for a political crime, he'd get rid of me at once. He'd report me to Berlin for interfering with the course of justice and eight days later I'd be facing a so-called People's Court for disloyalty myself. And it wouldn't even have done the man I'd let off any good.'

'It's easier for me,' I said, 'I could always declare a normal man to be of unsound mind, without having to bother the People's Court.'

'Aren't your reports checked?' asked Dr Hermann.

'Who is there to check them?' I replied. 'My commanding officer, the Senior Luftwaffe Medical Officer for this region, knows nothing about psychiatry. I'd be surprised if he even read my reports. To check their accuracy and authenticity he'd have to examine the patient himself and compare his findings with my own. It's never occurred to him to do such a thing. As my superior officer all he cares about is whether I behave properly as a soldier, whether I salute correctly, am properly dressed, wash my neck when I go to see the General, and begin and end my letters in the prescribed military jargon—but he'd never dream of interfering with my activities as a psychiatrist. As a lower-ranking officer I'm simply a worm to be trodden on from time to time in accordance with the old Prussian custom, but as a psychiatrist I'm completely independent.'

'I envy you your independence,' said Dr Hermann. 'But aren't you bound by any regulations? Is your only duty in giving judgment towards your conscience? Do you realise how lucky you are?'

I didn't understand him. My only duty towards my con-science? I didn't like these high-sounding phrases. To avoid giving an answer, I said:

'Anyhow, one can't really generalise about the state of mind induced by malaria. Each case must be considered on its merits.'

'Then,' said Dr Hermann, 'I recommend that tomorrow morning you come to the trial which is causing me so much anxiety. The Hasenloher case may interest you. The best thing would be for you to study the documents this evening.'

Chapter 28

/\

'Proceedings against Lance Corporal Ernst Hasenloher, No. 3 Interpreters' Company,' I read on the cover of the file. The man was accused of undermining the morale of the Wehrmacht. On the 27th April, 1944, while in the hospital at Varese, Lance Corporal Hasenloher made a number of slanderous remarks about German and Italian officers. As soon as there was trouble at the front, he had said, all the Italian officers had crawled away into their foxholes. German officers, he declared, were sending crates of goods back home. It was doubtful whether these had always been acquired in a regular manner. The troops had always done their duty, but the officers had only cared about eating and drinking, at least behind the lines. And even those officers who had done their duty bravely at the front, gave the impression of being far from convinced of the justice of their cause when they came back on leave. All seemed to have adopted the slogan: 'Let's enjoy the war while we can, the peace will be terrible.'

'On interrogation,' I read on, 'Lance Corporal Hasenloher declared that he had no recollection of the incident at all. Besides, such remarks would have been entirely foreign to his character. He thought that German officers did their duty bravely. He had never had any reason to change his opinion of them. When asked, therefore, to account for the above remarks, he said that he had been struck down by a severe attack of malaria the day before he made them. He had first had malaria while on the southern Italian front. His temperature had sometimes been as high as 100 degrees. During the days when he had no fever, he was completely exhausted.

'Hasenloher made these remarks which must be construed as prejudicial to the morale of the Wehrmacht,' continued the statement, 'in the presence of witnesses. Dr P. has made a report on diem to the court. As a rider to his evidence he has said that on the day on which Hasenloher chose to besmirch the honour of German officers, he had no fever. There could be no connection between his remarks and his illness. Unbalanced states of mind were unknown in malaria, above all in the intervals when there was no fever'.

I gave the documents back to the Judge Advocate.

'You've already got a medical report,' I said. 'It answers the question about the effect of malaria on the patient's state of mind clearly enough.'

'That doesn't matter,' said Dr Hermann. 'It's the oral evidence which counts at the trial. Besides as psychiatric consultant to the Senior Luftwaffe Medical Officer, your report will carry more weight. Are you coming to the trial?'

'Certainly I'll come,' I promised, 'but I can't allow my conscience to interfere with my evidence. I'm just a doctor, that's all.'

'So, you want to watch me commit a murder?' said Dr Hermann. 'Well, I hope you enjoy it.'

Shortly afterwards I said good-bye to Dr Hermann and went off through the soft Italian night to Gallarate, to find my billet. The place was completely blacked-out and I found myself in the neighbourhood of some factory where an army unit was stationed. In the yard, in the beam of a truck's head-lamps, a group of men were standing round a figure lying on the ground. Someone was kneeling beside him. I walked into the yard.

'Attention! Officer approaching!' shouted the sentry on the gate.

'What's the matter?' I asked, going up to the group.

'Someone's not well, sir, our medical orderly's just seeing to him.'

'Let me have a look at the man,' I said, 'I'm not just an Officer, I'm a doctor and perhaps I can help.'

I was standing outside the beam of the searchlights.

The orderly stood up and came over to me.

'Medical Corporal Degenbrück, sir,' he reported. 'The man's circulation has failed, sir. I can hardly feel his pulse.'

'Degenbrück?' I said. 'Did you say Degenbrück?'

'Yes, sir.'

'Vossmenge is the name. I think we've met before. But I'll have a look at the man, first.'

I examined the colouring of his membranes by the light of my torch. They were almost white. The pupils of his eyes hardly reacted.

'Bring him into the guard room,' I ordered. 'I'll get an injection ready.'

I always carried an emergency pack of medical equipment about with me.

A few minutes later Medical Corporal Degenbrück and I were sitting alone together by the unconscious man's side. His pulse was still weak but could now be felt quite distinctly. The membranes slowly began to turn pink.

'So, a man had to collapse to bring us together again,' I said.

'Yes, sir.'

'A murky factory yard in Gallarate wasn't exactly the place I'd expected to find my Orange Pastor.'

'No, sir.'

'Do stop saying "Yes, sir" and "No, sir". Don't you remember what you used to call me?'

'Yes sir.'

'What?'

'If the Major will permit, I previously took the liberty of addressing the Major as ... that is to say, in the days before the Major was the Major ...'

'Orange Pastor, it does you no credit to keep on talking to me in the third person like this. What's happened to you? The army seems to have turned you into a Yes-man.'

'For goodness' sake, Wind Doctor, I've only learnt to keep my mouth shut. I assume that the cause you serve is a different one from mine.'

We had spoken rather loudly. Our patient had come round again. I had to see to him. Half an hour later his condition was so much improved that we were able to take him by ambulance to the hospital at Varese. On the way back to Gallarate I said to Medical Corporal Degenbrück:

'So, you've stopped being a Pastor altogether. You now seem to be every inch a soldier.'

'Don't deceive yourself, Doctor, it's all camouflage.'

'You still owe me an answer to a question, Orange Pastor,'

I said. 'Do you remember the last time we met, five years ago in my office? You asked me then what my attitude was, as a Christian, to sterilisation. I replied with another question, namely: what has Christianity to do with sterilisation? I then answered your question. You never answered mine.'

'That's all a long time ago,' said Pastor Degenbrück and for the first time he seemed really to have forgotten that I was senior to him in rank. 'To-day we've got other problems. What I wanted to talk to you about then was the true freedom of a Christian.'

'The true freedom of a Christian?'

'Sterilisation is an interference with a man's freedom. It differs fundamentally from all other such forms of interference. The Bible says: "Now the Lord is that Spirit, and where the Spirit of God is, there is liberty." You thought I'd say God is the Law, didn't you? We've always been at cross purposes. But you wouldn't have had it otherwise, and all that's necessary is for us to define our different points of view. By freedom you mean a release from moral laws. But what I mean by freedom is dedication to the laws of culture and human dignity. Yes, human dignity, I said. Sterilisation is directed against a man's most intimate form of freedom, and it destroys his dignity. I don't suppose you understand that. I used to think that a good doctor like you was necessarily a man of culture. But by culture I mean the direction of a man's efforts towards the achievement of a true freedom of the spirit. When I saw you in your office squirming and wriggling in defence of the Anti-Christ I gave up all hope. You've taken the wrong turning. Your smart intellect wasn't smart enough to help you make the decision which we all have to make at some time or other in our lives.'

'What decision is that?'

'A decision that springs from our own inner freedom of spirit and for which you alone are responsible. A decision which no one can alter, a decision which will bring you nothing but loneliness in this world, the loneliness of a creature lost in the desert. A decision which disregards your material and worldly welfare, which is against all practical commonsense, a decision which must be made at the expense of all that is most dear to you in life, the decision, in short, which will lead you to God.'

'And how am I to know when the moment for this decision arrives?' I asked. 'Every day I have to take some decision, and a human life often depends on it. This evening for instance: that man might have died if I had given him the wrong injection. Provided I took the right decision, his life was assured for a little longer.'

'I knew you wouldn't understand me, Major,' said Pastor Degenbrück. 'The sort of decisions you mean don't spring from your inner freedom at all. You only think they do. In fact, these are just automatic responses which have been carefully conditioned in you. In such and such a case you give such and such an injection. If you give the wrong injection, you demonstrate your incompetence but not your freedom of spirit, for you had no intention of killing the man.'

'So, if I were to kill someone with the full intention of doing so I would be free. That's a paradoxical view to hear from a Pastor. I thought the Bible said: "Thou shalt not kill".'

'Yes, that is what it teaches. I did know that. I was only taking a hypothetical case. You could put it the other way round: you would be acting freely if with the full intention of doing so you were to save the life of a man whom the earthly law had condemned to die. I only wanted to show you that what you called decisions were in fact no more than the ordinary functional activity which dominates most men's lives. Men act without thinking, quite automatically, according to a pattern that has been instilled into them. The hideous thing is that it's perfectly easy to persuade them that they're acting freely. Their behaviour has been prescribed, for them down to the smallest detail and they comply splendidly. If by any chance they find themselves in a situation for which no pattern of behaviour has been prescribed, they become unsure of themselves. Can you imagine yourself in a situation in which, against all rules and regulations, against all habit, yes and even apparently against reason, you take a decision which allows you to escape from the narrow confines of your destiny—the destiny which in fact is not a destiny at all in the true sense of the word, but only a functional pattern of existence?'

'It's strange,' I said, 'Earlier this evening a judge Advocate told me that he envies me my independence.' I told the Pastor about the Hasenloher case. 'The man has said things which are held to undermine the morale of the Wehrmacht, and this is an offence which is always very severely punished. The man has only two chances: to be let off altogether or to be condemned to death. If I say that he was suffering from a temporary derangement of the mind, a possibility which doesn't arise in malaria—as the court already knows from the evidence before it—the Judge will be able to stop the case. But am I justified in misusing science like this?'

'And anyway, he has made statements which undermine the morale of the Wehrmacht, hasn't he, Major?' said the Pastor. 'Things would come to a pretty pass if we allowed ourselves to tolerate crimes of this sort, wouldn't they? Don't you feel that an attempt to undermine the morale of the Wehrmacht must be properly punished?'

'That's exactly what I'm thinking. If, by making false use of my position as a psychiatrist, I stop a criminal from getting the punishment he deserves, then my action only aids the enemy. I too will become a traitor to the cause.'

'Provided of course that we have a cause.'

'Who am I to decide whether this war is justified or no? I didn't want the war, and besides I'm a doctor: I'm neutral. I've only fired one shot in the whole of my military career. And that was at an empty tin on a heap of rubble.'

We had arrived at Gallarate by now.

'What am I to do?' I asked the Pastor. 'Am I justified as a Christian in helping a criminal escape punishment because that punishment seems to me too severe? Does your Church demand that I should? Think of the risk I'm running! The prosecutor will certainly know all about the first medical report, according to which Hasenloher's mind was in no way deranged. If my evidence contradicts this, he can ask for a third opinion. It may then come out that I've betrayed, my convictions as a doctor to save a criminal from punishment.'

'Well, Doctor, it's a Christian's duty to try and help every man in distress, but no one has ever said that a Christian should get himself into trouble for the sake of another. On the contrary it's a man's duty not to risk his life unnecessarily. Besides you're inwardly convinced that Hasenloher should be punished. Even if you did help him to escape punishment, you would be betraying your own convictions. That isn't the freedom I meant. Your action would represent simply a moving example of a soul touched by pity, but as you would be betraying your convictions there would be something contradictory and uncertain about it. A decision of this sort, motivated solely by pity, would not bring about any fundamental change in your inner being, it would merely take place on the edge of your outer self. What use would that be? The decision that I mean, the decision for true inner freedom, can only be made in the whole of your being. It must completely change you. Farewell, you windy doctor!'

'Good night, Orange Pastor,' I said. 'It isn't easy to be a good man. To be a good Christian seems to me almost impossible.'

Chapter 29

‘We will now hear the psychiatrist,’ said Dr Hermann, the Judge Advocate.

He looked at me expectantly, as if it were for me to say whether or not he must pass another death sentence.

The accused had made a sympathetic impression on the court. He had answered questions in a calm matter-of-fact way. Dr Hermann had sketched out the accused's career for us. Born in Bielefeld he had been trained in business and had emigrated to Italy long before the war. He loved the Italians for their humanity. He said something about them which made me stop and think. ‘Humanity,’ he said, ‘comes naturally to the Italian. He doesn't have to acquire it as we Germans do. Humanity is the one civilised quality which every man should possess. In many countries you have a small class of highly civilised people on the one side and the uncivilised masses on the other. In Italy the simplest man in the street is civilised because he has absorbed humanity with his mother's milk.'

There was no doubt that Hasenloher had spoken his mind when he made the remarks of which he was accused. They had expressed his thoughts exactly. Malaria had simply loosened his tongue. In his exhaustion he had no longer had the strength to hide his feeling of rage against the officers. Couldn't it be said then that malaria was the cause of his offence? Unfortunately, these were insufficient grounds for a plea of diminished responsibility. On the other hand, didn't many men think as he did? Thoughts are free. It is only words, spoken words, which are not. The man who could keep his tongue under control went unpunished.

Hadn't Hasenloher spoken the truth? Hadn't Italian officers in North Africa and Sicily shown themselves quite uninterested in the war? Didn't the whole of Badoglio's army go over to the enemy in the end? Weren't we Germans in fact very skilled at turning the war to our own material advantage behind the lines? Could you blame us? Perhaps Hasenloher had done no more than speak the truth. So that was his crime, that he had spoken the truth.

Was Hasenloher a criminal? He was a well-known fishery-expert. Many European countries had asked his advice on technical problems. What had the war to do with him?

'The psychiatrist!'

Everyone looked at me to see what my decision would be. This was it then: the decision.

'Gentlemen of the Court Martial!' I began. 'We have all had a chance of hearing how the accused expressed himself, of noting his particular turns of phrase. There is something gentle, considerate and sensitive both about his statement and his answers. If you compare this with the remarks of which he is accused, you notice at once how extraordinarily coarse and primitive they seem. Crude utterances of this sort by such an essentially gentle soul can only be ascribed to an exceptional condition of mind. And the exceptional condition of mind in the present case is determined by external circumstances. To-day the accused finds himself in an extremely dangerous situation. He must reckon with a severe penalty. Indeed, we know that he has to reckon with the death penalty. And yet he sits calmly before us as if nothing could happen to him. The accused feels mentally sure of himself. Not even the uncertainty of his fate can unsettle him. He shows no signs of fear. He doesn't even try to beg for mercy; he knows that it could do him little good. He is completely master of himself.

'How different things were when he made these subversive remarks. Then he was excited, completely beside himself 'out of his senses' as the graphic phrase has it. He just said anything that came into his head. He was quite out of control. And yet he was lying in hospital at the time. He had no apparent reason to get excited. The experiences on which his disparaging remarks about the officers were based lay behind him. Why should he suddenly have become so excited there in that hospital? And why was this outburst of his so primitive and out of character?

'Gentlemen! Mental disturbance is not normally associated with malaria, apart from the delirium which accompanies the fever. When the accused made this outburst, he was not suffering from fever. But listen to this account of the physical hardship to which the accused has been exposed: he first caught malaria in August last year at Sosenza; the doctors prescribed convalescent leave, but his commanding officer was unable to grant this, for his services as an interpreter were indispensable; in December he caught malaria again, in the most dangerous form in which it is known in Italy. Again, an application for convalescent leave was refused. Finally on top of the malaria he got a particularly stubborn boil for which he had to go to hospital. In March this year he had another bout of malaria. His unit was in retreat at the time. The circumstances were exceptional and exceptional demands were made on the men. It wasn't until 26th April that the accused was brought into the hospital at Varese. If, gentlemen, you refer to the date on which the accused committed the offence for which he is now on trial you will see that he had been in hospital exactly one day when he gave way to the excited outburst which he says to-day he can no longer remember.

'Gentlemen! I took the opportunity last night of talking to the young doctor to whom this outburst of Hasenloher's was first reported and who later submitted evidence of it to the court. This young colleague of mine has never been at the front. He doesn't know the physical and mental stresses to which the troops are exposed. Nor does he know anything of the different forms of sickness to which such stresses may give rise. He was therefore compelled to make out his report according to the textbooks: "Mental disturbance is not associated with malaria." Why is it not associated with it? Because, in the hospitals in which my young colleague learnt his medicine, in the first place there were no cases of malaria and in the second no cases of total and absolute exhaustion. I myself have never experienced a case of mental disturbance in malaria, but do I therefore have the experience to say that the accused cannot have been suffering from mental disturbance? We psychiatrists speak of "primitive reactions" which can be observed in very bad cases of illness among those patients who are particularly subject to them. The accused does not have the sort of constitution we have learnt to associate with such reactions. But a constitution isn't a fixed thing that one carries about with one like a piece of armour. Under particularly severe pressure a man's constitution can alter, that is to say the body can react in a different way from what one would have expected. In short, I am addressing you now as a doctor who has made a new discovery. This case has enriched my medical experience. I am able to diagnose in the accused a classic case of pathological primitive reaction originating solely in the sum of the external influences to which he has been subjected. I am quite certain that at the moment when he committed this offence, he was suffering from a mental disturbance equivalent to one involving the loss of all sense of responsibility.'

The trial was stopped immediately. The accused was given the benefit of Section 51 Paragraph I of military regulations.

The trial had been held in public and Medical Corporal Degenbrück had attended it.

'Doctor,' he said, 'you lied as no spiritual mountebank has ever lied before—with finesse, with a feeling for the psychological susceptibilities of the judges, in short with genius! You thought of everything. It was magnificent.'

'I didn't lie,' I said. 'I was firmly convinced of every word I said. Why should you imagine I lied? I've simply started thinking for myself.'

Chapter 30

I was busy at the prison at Gallarate all day. When I eventually made my way home to my billet, I found Pastor Degenbrück there waiting for me.

'I'd like a word with you, Doctor.'

He greeted me without any show of military formality. I felt like saying, 'Very good, Corporal.'

'I've been thinking about you, Wind Doctor,' he said. 'May I ask you something?'

'Ah, here it comes,' I said, 'the crucial question.'

'You might have guessed it was coming.'

'I don't like discussing it. So, you want to convert me?'

'It would be well worth while. But I had the impression at the trial to-day that it might no longer be necessary.'

'Do you think that I became a Christian in your sense of the word overnight?'

'A Christian in my sense of the word? There could be

worse things than that. But have I ever tried to convert you to any particular view of God?'

'My dear Orange Pastor,' I said, 'you're not one of those padres who always seem to me like the agents of some heavenly secret society. Whenever a colleague of yours tries to approach me as a man of the world, because he thinks he has a better chance of converting me that way, I always feel it would become him better if he wore uniform honorably, like the Salvation Army. There are two things however that I can't stand about you Protestant pastors. In the first place, in your sermons, you either consciously or unconsciously refuse to admit that the world has in any way changed or developed since the days of Christ. If Christ were to come down among us to-day he'd speak to us in an entirely different language from two thousand years ago.'

'Tell me one word of Christ's that isn't applicable to us to-day,' Pastor Degenbrück interrupted, me. 'That's the whole miracle: His words are valid for all eternity.'

'That's no reason why a preacher should talk in parables to-day.'

'You said there were two things you couldn't stand about Protestant pastors. What's the second one?'

'The other is the impossible way in which every Protestant pastor expounds the Bible just as the sense strikes him. Talking in parables in Lutheran German and radiating simplicity and goodness like that, you turn yourselves into caricatures!'

'Where did you last see a caricature of this sort?' asked the Pastor, laughing openly.

'In my parents' house,' I said. 'The local pastor often used to come there. He thought all men were as harmless and naive as he was himself. To him the world was a garden created by God, which would be a perfect paradise if only men would do their duty and go to Church. He had absolute confidence in the goodness of God, who he thought would reward him for his piety on this earth. The way in which God did in fact reward him seemed to him illogical. His daughter went off with a social democrat publisher and his son became a professional boxer.'

'There's nothing wrong with being a professional boxer,' said the Pastor. 'Still, I think I see what you mean. A pastor is subject to doubt, like everyone else. Tell me, did the pastor in your parents' village at least learn from the fate of his family in any way?'

'I don't think so. He remained the same naive child of God. But he took to drink in an innocent sort of way.'

'And this was the lost sheep who confirmed you?'

'No, he was replaced before that. The new pastor preached at us that we were all corrupt, that every one of our thoughts and deeds was sinful and that we should all go to hell if we didn't have true faith.'

'And unfortunately, you didn't have it?'

'Where was I to get it from? My parents never spoke to me about such things. The same grace was always said automatically when we sat down to meals. I was sent to Church on Sundays. At the main Christian holidays, I put on my best suit and was given a special meal at which there was usually plenty to eat. There were cakes on Sundays, and on Sunday afternoons the family went for a walk or someone paid us a visit. Sunday was the one day I dreaded in life, and I still dread it, for boredom is the most terrible thing in the world.'

'Which was the most boring? The walk? Or the visitors?'

'I'm sorry to have to admit it,' I said, 'but the most boring thing on Sundays was the service.'

'That's what I thought you'd say. I understand only too

well. And what about your scripture teachers in school?'

'We had very modern teachers. I learnt a lot at my school. But I hardly remember anything about the scripture lessons. I took Christianity and a belief in God for granted. It would never have occurred to me to question what I was told about such things. That all changed in my last year at school.'

'Can you remember the first time you began to have doubts?'

'Very clearly. Our scripture teacher told us that if we prayed hard during the week and read our Bibles God would send us fine weather on Sundays. But that didn't tally with our meteorological observations or with other ideas we had formed of the world.'

'Besides rain is one of God's gifts, too. So, you plumped for meteorology rather than religion?'

'There you have the typical dilemma of any young man of the twentieth century, my dear Orange Pastor. I decided for science as against religion.'

'That's not quite it, Wind Doctor. You don't put it quite right. Religion is an abstract concept. You must say that you decided for science as against God.'

'No. I decided for science as against your God.'

Pastor Degenbrück jumped up and embraced me.

'It delights me to hear you say that,' he said, laughing. 'It gives us a basis for agreement.'

He saw how astonished I was by his reaction.

'You've been avoiding the crucial question so far. But when you say that you don't believe in my God, you automatically admit that you do believe in *a* God.'

'A God who, as I said, is not your God.'

'What do you know of my God? You were introduced to religion by indifferent parents and cretinous teachers. You turned your face against a form of Christianity which had become fossilised in ritual. You didn't want to believe in a God who allowed the sun to shine so that good citizens could take their Sunday walks. This God, who you could only suppose was the eternal God of our Protestant faith, isn't my God either. You fled from the God of the petty bourgeois to science in search of something that every man needs: spiritual authority. From then on you worshipped scientific truth and held it to be the highest form of authority. Time, space and causality became your gods. But at the Hasenloher trial to-day you proved that this authority was not enough for you.'

'Why bring in the Hasenloher trial? All I did was to help the Judge Advocate get a wretched culprit off the death sentence.'

'You weren't just thinking of the Judge Advocate. Why do you pretend to be so modest? You saved the life of a doomed man; you can't get away from it. But how? By proving that psychiatry can prove anything. You want to convince me that you really believed all you said about the connection between malaria and his subversive remarks? I can't accept it. Perhaps you are just shy of admitting how useful psychiatry can be.'

'Why do you attach so much importance to the distinction? Isn't it enough that Hasenloher got off?'

'It's no longer a question of Hasenloher. The case is over. There's more at stake now. You were moved by a consciousness of God's mercy to come to the rescue of a doomed man. It's the duty of a Christian to do that, and you are a Christian even though you don't want to admit it. I wouldn't make such a fuss about what you had done if there wasn't something more to it. Listen: the original object of military justice was to maintain discipline. But this has long ago been lost sight of. Its object now is to bolster up a doomed regime, to

227

prolong a war that is already lost. No one who gets caught up in the judicial machine now stands a chance. Nearly all the judges are revolted by the bloody work they have to do, but there's no escape for them either. They could refuse to pronounce sentence of death. But they would only be sending themselves to the gallows by doing so and helping no one. If they were to obey their instincts and go on strike, they would merely be sacrificing themselves in vain. On the other hand, the technique you used at to-day's trial shows that there's a way by which the edge of this tyrannical justice can be blunted. Are you prepared to extend this technique and use it systematically?'

'My dear Orange Pastor,' I replied, 'don't you remember the discussions we used to have about what a ruthless impersonal force psychiatry was? In those days at the mental clinic, you were always trying to have madmen declared sane; am I now to declare sane men mad?'

'What I was against was the use of psychiatry to shut men up and deprive them of their lives. But I've no objection to it if it's used to give men freedom and save their lives. Well? Do you see now where your duty lies?'

'I'd prefer to apply my psychiatry to the men responsible for this tyrannical system rather than their perfectly sane victims.'

'But since we can't get at those who hold the power, we'll have to approach the problem this way. Do you agree?'

'Last night, when I asked you what I should do in Hasenloher's case you advised me not to do anything which conflicted with my intellectual conscience.'

'How could I guess your motive in wanting to help Hasenloher? I thought that pity was forcing you to do something against your better judgment, something that you would soon regret.'

'Is pity then such a bad motive? Do you attach no value to it?' I asked.

'Pity usually springs from soft-heartedness, Doctor,' said the Pastor. 'There's nothing wrong with it at all, but it's too unreliable. Pity is a confused feeling of the moment. What you had to do demanded something more than that. And you have that something more. To-day I know it. I didn't know yesterday. Well, are you prepared?'

'What do you mean by "something more"? Perhaps it isn't anything more than pity.'

'This something more is your love of humanity. But I asked you whether you were prepared to follow up your attitude of to-day. Or was it merely a flash of insight that will never be repeated?'

'You speak as if you were representing a group of conspirators. What can I do? I think that if psychiatry really can be used to help the innocent, then one ought to take advantage of the fact as long as possible.'

'Excellent. But it's going too far to talk about a group of conspirators. I've been in touch with the Catholic clergy of Gallarate. They've told me that some of the remnants of their troops who are now up before German courts martial are men who dispersed of their own accord after the Armistice. They were picked up by German military police and are being tried by the Germans.'

'The penalty for desertion is death in any army,' I said.

'But this isn't desertion, doctor,' said Pastor Degenbrück. 'The Italians aren't bound by any oath to the Germans. Marshal Badoglio, their former Commander in Chief, has disbanded the army and ordered men in areas temporarily occupied by the Germans to find their own way home. Most of them are now doing so. What else can you expect?'

'The Italians have certainly been under arms longer than we have,' I said.

'What possible sense could there be in shooting these fellows for desertion? Their only wish was to get home to their mothers. We'll reap nothing but hatred for ourselves and won't shorten the war by a single day.'

'You mean they could be saved from their fate if I declared them mentally unbalanced?'

'I trust you to handle the matter with skill.'

'But what am I to do? Go to each Judge Advocate who has an Italian deserter to try and say: "Your prisoner is perfectly fit and normal, but I'd like to make out a psychiatric diagnosis for him so that you can let him off"?'

'We mustn't go about it as clumsily as that. I'll take on the job of contacting the Judge Advocates. You don't need to know how I do it. Whenever you find yourself asked to decide whether an Italian soldier is accountable for his actions or not, you'll know what to do.'

'But I can't label every member of the Italian army who tried to escape from us a schizophrenic!'

'You must use some variety in your methods,' said Pastor Degenbrück. 'A little imagination is all that's needed. I shall trust to psychiatry and to your extraordinary gift for making a scientifically based hypothesis seem plausible, however absurd it may be.'

'You're turning me into what you've already accused me of being once to-day, Pastor: a spiritual mountebank!'

'But remember that we're both acting in a good cause. A pure scientist like yourself will always seem a spiritual mountebank to me. I think a great deal of the natural sciences. I don't think a great deal of those natural scientists who so typically confuse causality with the working of the Holy

Spirit. However, if it's for a good cause, then I'm prepared to regard natural scientists as the most important pillars of our civilisation.'

Chapter 31

The first Italian soldier I had to investigate was Angelo Micanti. He came from Montefarco near Perugia. He was forty-one. His father was dead, his mother old. She had no one but him to support her in her old age. But Angelo had to go off to the war. He took part in the campaigns in Albania and Southern Italy. When the King finally imprisoned Mussolini—the one Italian who wanted the war—Angelo hoped he would be able to go home, but the Germans wouldn't let him go and attached him to a *flak* company near Bologna. One day he made off and tried to get home over the Appenines. But a Fascist police patrol caught him and brought him back to Bologna.

Angelo had never been to school. He had had to look after his brother and two small sisters while his mother went to work. Later on, his mother became ill, and Angelo had to go to work to feed the family. He got a job looking after turkeys.

Then he inherited a little farm worth about ten thousand lire. But neither he nor his sisters—his brother had died—knew anything about agriculture. Besides they needed money for the doctor, for their mother was very sick. So, Angelo sold his farm for ten thousand lire. But on the same day as he received the money, he got to know a girl in Perugia whom he found attractive. Now that he had so much money, he was able to think about getting married for the first time. When the girl said she didn't want to marry a stupid shepherd boy like him, he showed her the money. She immediately saw sense and promised to marry him. He went off with her to a man who she said was the Prefect. The supposed Prefect asked him if he wanted to marry the girl. He was only too happy to say yes. In that case he must hand over the money to her as a surety, and he would marry them both at once. He handed over the money without any misgiving, for it would be remaining in the family. Then the Prefect went ahead with the marriage and read the marriage contract through to them. Angelo made three crosses at the bottom of it for he could neither read nor write. Then the couple separated. The two of them were to go off the next day to Montefarco where his mother had a little tumble-down house. But the next morning the bride had disappeared. At the house of the supposed Prefect nothing was known of any marriage at all. Angelo went off to find the Mayor, who told him that he had been caught by a swindler for he was the only person who had any right to perform a civil marriage. What was the girl's name? But Angelo didn't know; he had forgotten to ask her full name.

My report ran as follows: 'Angelo Micanti is feeble-minded. The accused certainly knew that he was exposing himself to punishment by running away from his unit without permission. But he is hardly in a position to appreciate the significance of his action. The range of his thoughts hardly extends beyond the horizon of his Umbrian mountain village. His mentality is that of an imbecile. There can be no question of holding him responsible for his actions.'

Then I was called to Verona. The old Fort St. Leonardo, a compact and massive rectangular building which had been put up by Radetzky at the time of the fortification of the Alps had now been turned into a Wehrmacht prison. This was where Ardito Cordivi lay. He had been enrolled as an auxiliary soldier in the German Luftwaffe. He was caught wandering about without any papers near Sommacampagna. He was wearing civilian clothes. His excuse was that he thought the war was over. He had heard it on the radio. That was all that could be got out of him. But it was known that his parents were dead and that he had been brought up in the 'Cesare Lombroso' orphanage in the Via Lenotti in Verona. This was lucky for him as the orphanage housed mostly feeble-minded and epileptic children. I couldn't give another diagnosis of feeble-mindedness. The Orange Pastor had suggested that I should introduce a little variety into my work. So Ardito Cordivi was declared an epileptic. I hope he will forgive me!

I didn't have to invent any diagnosis for Guido Servalle, born on 24th August 1924 in San Fioro. He really was feeble-minded. He had been a sort of mascot in his unit when it was still under Italian command. Everyone teased him, but at the same time he was protected and cared for like some sacred cow in India. He could do what he liked. He could lie asleep in the corridors of the barracks all day if he wanted to. No officer would have thought of waking him up. Even the Major stepped over him carefully. The Major's name was Gabriel and he saw to it that Guido wasn't teased too much. To Guido Major Gabriel was the most important person in the world. If Guido was asked: 'Who rules over heaven and earth?' he answered at once: 'Major Gabriel.' And when he was asked: 'Who was the last King of Italy?' he answered: 'Major Gabriel.' 'And who is the Lord of Hell?' 'Major Gabriel.' The only two towns in the whole world which Guido knew the names of were Venice and Grosseto. He had gone to Venice occasionally with his Lord and Master, Major Gabriel, when he was cleaning up the barracks at Mestre, and he had been born in Grosseto. He deserted when Major Gabriel was killed in an air raid. When caught, he said he was looking for Major Gabriel.

Alberto Rinfreschi from Piacenza presented a more difficult problem. His superior officer had called him a scoundrel. Alberto felt insulted, packed up his things and walked off. He was walking down the main road in full uniform when a Wehrmacht patrol picked him up. When he was interrogated, he said he had felt very queer when he left his unit but that was all he could remember. He tied himself up in knots, contradicted himself, and when he saw that he wasn't making a good impression, he went over to the offensive and maintained that Italy had never really been a genuine friend of Germany's. Italy had only pretended to fight the war. In fact, the Italian people were far closer in feeling to the French than the Germans. The fleet however was anglophile. Mussolini's mistake had been to try and persuade the Italians that they were the descendants of the ancient Romans. Italy was certainly a Romanesque country, but it no longer had anything in common with ancient Rome. The Romans were simply a philological concept. The Germans were Italy's enemies and so on.

It was thus impossible to say that Alberto Rinfreschi was feeble-minded. Fortunately, he had a brother and an uncle who had both been in lunatic asylums. So, he could be described as a schizophrenic. Statistically feeble-mindedness already preponderated in my list of false diagnoses. But since the impression Rinfreschi made was only one of slight nervousness I couldn't get him the benefit of Section 51 Paragraph I. It would have looked too obvious. There was too much at stake for our game to be jeopardised lightly. But even under Section 51 Paragraph II, which deals with cases of diminished responsibility he may have got off with it quite lightly. Unfortunately, I couldn't stay to the end of the trial. I had to get back to Gallarate where several cases were waiting to be cleared up. I am not in a position to give the names of the Italians whom we freed there.

'Operation Orange Pastor' went off without a hitch. We had already secured the release of about twenty-five Italians when the order to court-martial for desertion those Italian soldiers who had absconded was cancelled.

Chapter 32

When travelling on duty between Undine and Cuvio in the one direction, and Bolzano and Bologna in the other I often had occasion to admire the German Wehrmacht's incomparable organisation. What subtle measures were taken to deal with the petrol shortage for instance! Captain Kowalski of a Luftwaffe communications unit initiated me into the mysteries of the system.

'My company consists solely of technicians,' he said. 'All splendid fellows. It's their job to keep the telephone connection between the Brenner and the front on the Po in order. We're kept very busy, for the stretch on the Brenner is attacked by bombers or strafed by fighters almost every day. My men are strung out over the whole stretch. There are little groups of them all over the place between Bressanone and Ferrara. I sit here in Verona like a spider in the centre of a web. But even a spider sometimes has to venture out and see that the web is all right. Once a month I motor over the whole stretch to see what my men are up to. For that I need sixty litres of petrol.

'To be able to start I first have to get a movement order from my unit and a permit from the General. The movement order is checked by the military police along the route. The permit is given me by the General himself, since the Reichsmarshal has made him personally responsible for seeing that petrol is used only for essential journeys.

'I write out the movement order myself and get it signed by my Adjutant. The military police don't ask to see the General's permit, but on the other hand I can't get any petrol without it. All the petrol in Field Marshal Rommel's area is controlled by the army. The department which issues the petrol—on production, that is, of the General's permit—is at Sirmione on Lake Garda.

'In order to get the petrol, I apply for a permit entitling me to sixty litres. The application goes first to battalion headquarters which is at Affi, not far from Lake Garda. From there it goes up through the usual channels to regimental headquarters which are at Bolzano. From there it is sent to the divisional headquarters which are somewhere near here in the neighbourhood of Verona. Divisional headquarters then send it by despatch rider to the General at Malcesine. There the despatch rider takes it to the distributing officer in the despatch riders' centre. He sends it to the officer in charge of despatches at staff headquarters. From there it goes to the General's Adjutant and from there it finds its way at last onto the General's desk. The General signs the permit and gives it to his Adjutant. The Adjutant sends it back to divisional headquarters, via the officer in charge of despatches and the despatch riders' centre whence it comes back to Verona.

From there it goes to regimental headquarters at Bolzano and from there to battalion headquarters at Affi. And from there it comes back to me at Verona again.'

'So that at last you can set off,' I said, interrupting the Captain.

'What do you mean, Doctor?' said the Captain. 'I've only got the permit so far. I've now got to get the petrol. I have to send the permit to Sirmione where the petrol is issued. It takes a week before I get my application back.'

'Thank God for that anyway,' I said with relief. 'Now at last you really can be off.'

'How do you make that out, Doctor?' said the Captain. 'The application is always refused the first time. Colonel Zimmerman of the Army Administrative Branch maintains that the Luftwaffe should, fly and not travel by car.'

'So, you can't go, then? And your men never see their commanding officer?' I asked.

'What an idea! I have to see my men at all costs. It's my one and only task in this farcical war!'

'So, you go on foot?'

'You can't ask me to go from Bressanone to Ferrara on foot. No one's done that since Barbarossa's time.'

'But you said you were refused your petrol?'

'When I get my rejected application back from Colonel Zimmerman, I tell the General what has happened. My complaint goes up through the usual channels from Verona to Affi to Bolzano, from there back to Verona and from there to Malcesine where it passes through the despatch riders' centre, the office of the officer in charge of despatches and the Adjutant's office to the General's desk. The General reads my complaint through and says: "What on earth's Colonel Zimmerman thinking of? Captain Kowalski's got to be able to visit his men!" So, he dictates a letter to Colonel Zimmerman: "Dear Colonel Zimmerman, Would you do me a personal favour and allow Captain Kowalski to have sixty litres of petrol? He has to visit his men at least once a month." The letter goes by special despatch rider to Sirmione. The General has plenty of petrol. Colonel Zimmerman in Sirmione reads the letter and says: "We can't very well deny the General anything!" So, he writes out a permit for me to have sixty litres of petrol. He gives the permit to a special despatch rider who takes it to the General at Malcesine. The General says: "Well why couldn't that have been done in the first place? Now Kowalski can get on with the job!" So he gives Colonel Zimmerman's note to his Adjutant who sends it back to me or rather to the officer i/c despatches whence it goes to the despatch riders' centre and from there to divisional headquarters at Verona, regimental headquarters at Bolzano, and battalion headquarters at Affi, finally coming back to me at Verona. And now at last I am in possession of a permit entitling me to sixty litres of petrol and now at last, Doctor, I can set off—that is, if there is any petrol to be had.'

'And how long does this elaborate paper war for sixty litres of petrol go on?' I asked Captain Kowalski.

'It takes exactly six weeks from the day on which I first make my application to the day on which I get the petrol.'

'But if it takes as long as that, you can't visit your unit after all,' I said.

'I'd be a bad unit commander if I didn't visit my men once a month.'

'Well, you don't go on foot. Perhaps you have a bicycle?'

'No, I go by car.'

'Without any petrol?'

'I buy myself petrol on the black market.'

'Are you as rich as that, Captain?' I asked.

'Not in money, but in copper wire, telephones and insulating material.'

'And what do you do with the petrol which you do get in the end, even though too late?'

'I use that for important journeys which the General mustn't know about.'

'I see: doing business with copper wire, for example?'

'I have to get to see my men. If I don't and one of the telephone lines is laid wrong, then I'm court-martialed. If I neglect my duty, I can't use the fact that I didn't have any petrol as an excuse.'

'It hardly makes any sort of sense at all,' I said. 'But why are you so strictly controlled?'

'Because they're afraid that I'll take Italian girls for joyrides.'

'But there's something wrong there, Captain,' I said. 'If they gave you sixty litres a month without any fuss, without permits, applications, coupons or anything like that, you could still only use it for one journey between Bressanone and Ferrara, couldn't you?'

'Quite right, Doctor, you've put it in a nutshell. I wouldn't have a drop over with which to take my girl for a ride.'

'But if in fact you were to neglect your duty and take her for a ride instead of visiting your men, the General still wouldn't be able to catch you, because you make out your own movement order and it's only the movement order which is controlled on the roads, isn't that so?'

'That is so, doctor.'

'So, all this elaborate supervision is completely useless, Captain.'

'It's very sharp of you to see that, Doctor. They've undoubtedly realised it at the various staff headquarters too.

But they're glad to have plenty of work to do up there, or other work might be found for them.'

'You mean at the front?'

'Where the bullets fly.'

Chapter 33

One hot July day in 1944 the Field Marshal's car had a puncture at Castelfranco. While his driver was changing the wheel the Field Marshal looked round the little town, of which the medieval fortifications were still intact. In a cloister-like building he discovered his air-force's medical supply base. When he suddenly walked unannounced into the guard room, the sentry was so frightened he dropped his rifle. 'Typical pill-merchant,' said the Field Marshal. 'Now put your rifle over in the comer and go and fetch your commanding officer.'

Senior Staff Chemist Peters led the Field Marshal through the halls of the cloister and showed him the stacked-up stores. 'And can your men defend all this aspirin?' asked the Field Marshal. Dr Peters reported that he had eight rifles and three hundred rounds of ammunition at his disposal.

'The Partisans occupy the mountain valleys twenty-five kilometres from here,' said the Field Marshal. 'You can't hope to hold this outfit against them with that. Find yourself another site, preferably in the neighbourhood of some unit with battle experience. I'm afraid that when the Partisans realise that they've a chance of equipping themselves with three years' medical supplies on the cheap here, it won't be long before they do something about it. You pill-merchants can't even hold a rifle. In eight weeks at the latest I want to hear from you that you've moved. Good morning.'

The Field Marshal climbed into his car and drove away.

It so happened that a large assembly centre for army recruits was moved to Castelfranco a few days later. The unit consisted of three hundred rifles and a number of machine guns. Senior Staff Chemist Peters immediately gave up looking for a suitable new building for his medical stores and reported to the Field Marshal's Senior Air Medical Officer that the move which the Field Marshal had ordered was no longer necessary.

In civilian life the Senior Staff Chemist's action would have been sensible and reasonable. Unfortunately, military people do things differently. Peters was reprimanded for his unmilitary behaviour by the Senior Air Medical Officer, Colonel Dr Kannengiesser. Of course he must move, and at once.

Senior Staff Chemist Peters was what is called a special commission officer. He hadn't been through the usual military career but was under contract to the Luftwaffe. He was given the rank of Major to correspond with his position, but only for the duration of his service as a specialist. So that he shouldn't be confused with a real major, his shoulder tabs were only half as wide as those of a real one. Likewise, the Senior Staff Chemist was only half a soldier (the other half of him was very much a civilian) and he still retained a sound portion of ordinary commonsense. When the order to move was repeated, he got on the telephone to Colonel Dr Kannengiesser and explained to him that the reason which had prompted the Field Marshal to give the order in the first place no longer existed. Besides, continued the Senior Staff Chemist to his commanding officer, he had searched far and wide for a site capable of holding the vast stores of the medical supply base but without success. The only possibility was an empty factory building in a village near Bassana, at the foot of Mount Grappa, but there again there was no military unit to give protection. If he were to move there, the supply base would be in the immediate vicinity of the Partisans and still quite undefended.

Colonel Kannengiesser had long grown out of the habit of thinking normally. He was unable to accept his chemist's reasonable objections. The Field Marshal's orders, he said, were to be carried out without fail.

'But couldn't you discuss the matter with the Field Marshal again?' cried Dr Peters down the telephone, apparently incapable of learning. 'The Field Marshal's order has lost its point now.'

'That's not for you to say,' said Colonel Dr Kannengiesser. 'Besides I can't advise the Field Marshal to withdraw an order. The Field Marshal's orders are not withdrawn. You will move at once. See to it that you take proper measures against the Partisans.'

Senior Staff Chemist Dr Peters moved to the foot of Mount Grappa. The Partisans sent him a message to the effect that though he enjoyed an extraordinary degree of respect among the Partisans on account of his readiness to help some of their wounded, they could not agree to him removing his medical supply base to the immediate vicinity of the mountain chain which they dominated, for they had learnt by experience that the supply base would soon be followed by active troops. He should remain where he was. No one would bother him in Castelfranco.

Senior Staff Chemist Peters was unable to heed the warning. As he drove at the head of his column into the little village where he was now to take up his quarters, he was met by a burst of Sten gun fire from a well-laid ambush. Hit by thirty-four bullets he fell back dead on the upholstery of his car.

It wasn't only among the Partisans that Senior Staff Chemist Peters had been popular. Nowhere was his death more regretted than in the hospital town of Riva. The doctors particularly praised his extraordinary skill in securing those medical supplies which were almost unobtainable as a result of the general shortage of raw materials at home. I had some business to do in Riva soon after Peters' death and two of the doctors there begged me to get Colonel Dr Kannengiesser sent home by the same means as I had employed with Colonel Strube. They had heard of my method from Major Dr Müller who was now in Riva with his hospital.

I explained why I had to refuse the demand. I said that conditions had been favourable for an extraordinary step of this sort in Rome where I had been on friendly terms with the General. But though I had met the Field Marshal once or twice in the course of my duty, I didn't really know him at all. My final reason for refusal was that I wasn't on the Field Marshal's staff. I wasn't even allowed to go and see him without first acquainting Colonel Dr Kannengiesser with the reasons for my visit.

Several weeks later I was unexpectedly ordered to report to the Senior Air Medical Officer. As a result, I had to miss an important trial in Verona where I was hoping to be able to use psychiatry to save an elderly Sergeant from the hangman. He had shouted out in a Verona tavern, for everyone to hear, that National Socialism was just as disgusting as Bolshevism.

I reported to Colonel Dr Kannengiesser's office in Salsomaggiore at the correct time.

'The Colonel has gone to a little party. He'll be back soon,' his sergeant told me.

It had taken me a whole day to get from Verona to Salsomaggiore. I was hungry and thirsty. I sat down on a chair in the ante-room of my commanding officer's office and waited. I waited from six o'clock in the evening to one o'clock in the morning. Then the telephone rang. The Sergeant, who had fallen asleep on a camp bed beside the telephone, picked up the receiver, gave his name and rank, said 'Very good, Colonel' several times and put the receiver back again. Then he turned to me and said: 'The Colonel is afraid he can't see you now. You're to come back at eight o'clock to-morrow morning.'

I was back again in the Colonel's ante-room at eight o'clock the next day. The Colonel did not appear. At eleven o'clock his Adjutant came in and told me that as a result of the party which had gone on late the night before the Colonel wasn't feeling very well and I should come back at two o'clock that afternoon. I visited the Salsomaggiore baths and ate my lunch. At two o'clock I reported again. I was asked to wait a little. The Colonel Doctor was not yet up. I waited. The Colonel Doctor appeared at six. He was drunk. In a series of disjointed sentences, he informed me that my activities as psychiatric consultant were extended to the whole regional command of the air force.

'And now, my dear Vossmenge, I'd like to acquaint you with my methods. They're the methods of the Hohenzollems: smart orders, prompt obedience, rigid military bearing!'

'And not a moment's peace for anyone, Colonel,' I said. 'I know the system.'

'Then we'll get on well together,' said the Colonel, and looked at me out of his blood-shot eyes in astonishment.

This seemed a good moment to apply the ruthlessness of psychiatry to the ruthlessness of the Sergeant-Major mentality.

'I hope you'll be satisfied with your psychiatric consultant, Colonel,' I said. 'If for instance you should be of the opinion that it is time to end once and for all the misuse of alcohol by senior staff officers, you would have my full support. What I have seen here in Salsomaggiore in the last twenty-four hours is in itself enough to justify a psychiatric diagnosis.'

'And what have you seen here, my little man?' asked the Colonel with a hypocritical smile.

'I had an opportunity of seeing that an important post, with responsibilities extending over the entire area under the Field Marshal's command was left without anyone in charge of it for twenty-four hours. The officer who should have been in charge was drunk. He still is.'

The Colonel turned pale, stood up, walked round the desk, came up to me and said: 'I've already heard one or two things about your extraordinary capabilities. But *caro mio*, you're on the *via falsa*. I don't think we will be getting on so well after all.'

And he dismissed me.

Chapter 34

Medical Corporal Degenbrück was committed to the military prison in Verona in the middle of October. Judge Advocate Dr Schröder, a member of the judicial department of the General in charge of Army Group C, begged me to examine the mental condition of the prisoner for he was liable to a heavy sentence. I gathered from what the Judge Advocate told me that he was anxious to get Degenbrück off as lightly as possible.

I took care not to let my willingness to help Degenbrück regain his liberty at all costs seem too obvious. I therefore expressed considerable reservations about giving a psychiatric opinion on the prisoner, for my competence was specifically limited to members of the Luftwaffe.

'I don't want to make you violate your duty in any way,' said Dr Schröder, 'but we're having certain administrative difficulties with our army psychiatrists just at the moment. The army possesses only one psychiatric department, at Arco, and it is in charge of a very conscientious university professor. The department functions almost as in peacetime. In order to obtain a psychiatric opinion from them, we have to send them the prisoner for six weeks' observation. To do that we have to provide a car and escort to take him to Arco and bring him back again six weeks later. But our judicial department has only one vehicle for the transport of prisoners and that is needed here almost every day, so we have to apply to Army Group Headquarters for transport and fuel twice, every time we send someone for examination, once for the journey there and once for the journey back. This causes a great deal of bother, so we usually dispense with the examination altogether.

'Now as far as your competence as psychiatric expert is concerned,' continued Judge Advocate Dr Schröder, 'all that is necessary for us is your agreement to examine a member of the army. We, as an army unit, shall be making claims on your services, so you need have no fear of complaints from us about your meddling in our affairs. The Luftwaffe has no cause for complaint either, since your sphere of responsibility is in no way infringed by your acting for the army, if, however, you feel unable to act outside it, there's nothing I can do about it.'

'I wouldn't be much of a doctor,' I replied, 'if I were to refuse to help a man merely because he belongs to the army. I've already watched this two-class system operating in the Wehrmacht with some misgiving. I didn't really regard the competition between the two branches of the services as ominous until one day in North Africa when I was in charge of a transport of wounded and I received the order to load up my bus with Luftwaffe wounded only and leave all members of the army lying out in the sun.'

'And what was your attitude to such an idiotic order?' the Judge Advocate asked me.

'I took no notice of it. I treated the evacuation of the wounded to hospital as a purely medical operation. As a doctor my only responsibility in medical matters is to my conscience. A doctor has an inalienable right to make his own decision about the best way to help the sick. That is what I was taught, and it has been the teaching of our profession for upwards of two thousand years.'

'I envy you your freedom to make your own decisions. The medical profession is the only one which has been able to stay independent. Its high standard of professional ethics has kept it together. That is why I come to you now, hoping that you won't deny me your help in the Degenbrück case.'

The Judge Advocate gave me the details of Medical Corporal Degenbrück's offence.

He had held a secret divine service in Gallarate, and at it he had begged God to give victory over the Anti-Christ to the Christian armies of Roosevelt and Churchill.

'The man must really be mad,' said Dr Schröder. 'What sane man would bring ruin on himself like this? Surely madness must he at the root of such religious fanaticism? In any case I've no great wish to make a martyr of the lunatic.'

I promised to examine the mad pastor the next day, and report to the Judge Advocate.

I had no eye for the charm of the landscape as I climbed up through the vineyards to the nearby Fort St. Mattia in which the prisoners awaiting trial were held. In the gloomy interior of the old well-preserved fortress I found Pastor Degenbrück in the best of form. The guard brought him into the primitively fixed-up medical consulting room and left him alone with me.

'So, you've cut yourself off from your own people, Orange Pastor,' I said. 'I hear you've been praying for the downfall of Germany.

'On the contrary, my dear Wind Doctor,' said Pastor Degenbrück, 'If you are referring to certain prayers of mine which have come to the ears of the court martial, I must put you right: I was praying to God for the spiritual exaltation of Germany. It's true I realise that God can't exalt us without first inflicting a military defeat on us. One can ask anything of God, but one must allow him to set about it logically. He can't save us from the Anti-Christ until the full extent of the man's evil has been brought home to us. Even Hitler is an instrument of God.'

'It's a queer sort of logic,' I said. 'For the Germans to be saved, must Germany first be destroyed? For Germany to be destroyed, must it be sent the Anti-Christ, as you call Hitler, and finally are the Germans to be. punished for following him?'

'I see that to a scientist it must sound senseless, and a psychiatrist will even regard it as a symptom of psychosis, but to our Christian view of history the life of both nations and of individuals is a test. Evil is created by God, so that we may recognise the good—but I assume you didn't come all the way up here to be instructed in the catechism.'

'Of course,' I said, 'I had something else in mind. Judge Advocate Dr Schröder, who is handling your case, has no particular inclination to turn you into a Christian martyr. In order to get you released he requires my support. You know from your own experience how psychiatry can be used to deprive a man of the doubtful pleasure of having his head removed.'

'So, Wind Doctor, at last you're in the position you've been hoping for ever since we first met: at last you're able to say I'm mad!'

'It will be a particular pleasure for me,' I replied, 'if I can use the opportunity to prevent the Protestant Church from losing a first-class pastor.'

'I won't stop you saving my life,' said the Pastor, 'so long as you abide by certain rules. If you are determined to get me out of this hole at all costs, then you must know that I will let myself be released only on very special conditions.'

'I'm grateful to you for not objecting to my rescuing you on principle anyway. Of course, I'm only too ready to examine your conditions. Provided that they demand nothing impossible of me, I'll respect your wishes.'

'In the first place,' said the Pastor, 'it's important to me that you should not say I'm mad. I feel mentally healthier than ever before. I shouldn't like suddenly to be thought mad now.'

'Why do you make things so difficult?' I asked. 'You know that the only way I have of getting you out of here is by casting some doubt on your reason.'

'I'm extremely sorry to have to make you respect my conditions. But I don't see why you should get the credit of saving a criminal from his punishment at my expense.'

'Does a life of freedom and dignity no longer mean anything to you then? Do you want to lie here and rot until they shoot you in the moat?'

'I can't purchase life and a questionable form of freedom with a lie. Once I am declared insane no one will listen to me anymore. To be thought mad is worse than being dead. A dead man can influence people from beyond the grave, by his writings, by what people remember of him, by the work he did in his life-time. A madman is dead as mutton even when he's still alive. His words are regarded as foolish babbling, his deeds mere clowning. Why should I prefer sentence of death on my living body to eternal life? Do you take me for a godless man, who sees life solely as a means of gratifying impulses?'

'But how am I going to get you out of here if you won't co-operate?' I asked. 'Let me remind you that you can be released even without your agreement. You've no right to perpetual imprisonment. Besides, if it's a death sentence you're hoping for, I must remind you that the court martial sometimes shrinks from that.'

'If, to help me to an existence which I deem to be of questionable value, you declare me irresponsible for my actions, I'll soon show you how easy it is to upset the opinion of a psychiatrist. I'll repeat the prayers for which I've been arrested in public, and I'll add that this activity is being carried out by permission of a psychiatrist who regards it as his professional duty to declare sane men mad.'

'All right,' I said. 'Then you force the court martial to commit an injustice and sentence you to death. I don't know that it's very Christian to prevent a judge from doing good when he wants to.'

'I'm not forcing anyone to shed blood, Doctor,' said Pastor Degenbrück. 'You misread my intentions. It is not I who am responsible for the system of military justice. I haven't said that I would refuse to leave this fortress. I've merely laid down the conditions on which I am prepared to be freed should God see fit to grant me freedom. I'm not going to let myself be given life by a piece of psychiatric crookedness. Allow me to ask one purely theoretical question: on what diagnosis would you think yourself most likely to snatch me from the hands of justice?'

'I've been thinking about that,' I said. 'Religious mania would probably be the most plausible.'

'How right I was to reject your offer. The whole point of religion is that it should be a conviction by which one is prepared to stand or fall. If you compare my religious convictions to a form of mania you must logically think that the faith I hold is also mad. A judgment of that sort is the sin against the Holy Ghost, even though it's made in what is meant to be a good cause. I can't accept your offer—I don't want to inflict on you the hellish tortures to which your conscience would be exposed.'

'Never has a suicide invented more fantastic arguments to justify his suicide,' I said angrily. 'You're being just as stubborn now as you were when you bought the twenty-five tons of oranges.'

'My dear Wind Doctor,' said the Pastor and he smiled, 'if you were not certain in your innermost being that my point of view is the right one, you wouldn't be trying so hard to save me from a fate which in fact holds no terrors for me.'

'Your attitude is at variance with the God-given instinct of self-preservation,' I cried, now extremely angry. 'Your way of trying to prove yourself sane is the most dangerous form of madness I've ever met.'

'You may well be right there,' said the Pastor. 'The sacred force of a faith founded in God has always proved stronger than scientific and philosophical dogma based on relative concepts. If to-day I have convinced you of the need to recognise the supremacy of the spirit in all situations and of the need to sacrifice one's life for it in certain circumstances then I haven't been incarcerated in one of the darkest and dampest of dungeons in vain.'

'If that's how it must be—then all right,' I said. 'But perhaps it needn't be like that. There are certainly other ways of keeping you with us. You'll be hearing from me.'

And I had him taken away.

Chapter 35

Judge Advocate Dr Schröder listened calmly to the account of my fruitless journey to Fort St. Mattia.

'There is in fact another way of saving this obstinate priest from martyrdom,' he said. 'The moment a doctor declares him unfit for arrest, I can release him and defer the trial.'

'What good would that do?' I said. 'He'll pray for the downfall of Germany again and be denounced again. At the new trial it will come out that you released him. And then you'll be brought to reckoning too.'

'Things won't be any better for you,' said the Judge Advocate, 'If it comes out that you've made a false medical report. So, we'll urge the mad pastor to fly to Switzerland as soon as he's released. I know a German Italian who'll take him over the frontier. Will you declare Degenbrück unfit for arrest?'

'As far as I know,' I said, 'a certificate of that sort has to be made out by the prison doctor. My only business is to decide whether the prisoner can be accounted responsible for his actions.'

'The prison doctor is a young man whose attitude we can't be sure of. I can't risk disclosing my views to him. You'll have to sign the certificate whether you're competent to do so or not.'

'And what are the chances of my interference in my colleague's business passing unnoticed?' I asked.

'If you take my advice, you'll write out the certificate on a Sunday. The prison doctor is off duty on Sundays. He usually goes for a little excursion into the country round Verona and doesn't come back until Monday. As soon as I get your medical certificate, I'll take the necessary steps to have Degenbrück released. If your colleague should notice that he's been by-passed when he gets back, I'll try and hold up his complaint. He'll have to put it in through the prison administration. But I doubt whether he'll notice the release of one of the many inmates of St. Mattia.'

'All right,' I said. 'Next Sunday then I shall thwart Pastor Degenbrück of his intention of going down to history as a martyr to his faith.'

Chapter 36

A light rain was falling as I climbed up to the Fort St. Mattia on the following Sunday. It was a long time before my ring at the bell was answered. The Sergeant on duty looked at me indifferently as I asked for the prisoner Degenbrück to be produced. Pastor Degenbrück was produced. I sent the guard out.

'Listen, Orange Pastor,' I said. 'Judge Advocate Dr Schröder doesn't want to burden his conscience by sentencing you to death. He will release you to-day, as soon as he gets a medical certificate declaring you unfit for arrest. I am now going to make out such a certificate. I'll give you a disease which won't insult your pride. From now on you are suffering from a nervous heart disease. If anyone should question you about this disease, describe the following symptoms: ever since your time at the front in Russia you've been subject to occasional violent spasms of pain in the region of the heart, accompanied by a feeling of extreme anxiety. These spasms occur with particular violence when you've been sub-jected to physical strain. You have to gasp for breath, have a strange feeling that the end is approaching and so on. Will you oblige us by co-operating in this little fraud?'

'It's not easy for me to comply with your request, Doctor. But I won't resist your efforts to release me any longer.'

'I'm delighted that you find the conditions of your return to freedom acceptable. As soon as you're out go to the offices of the judicial department at Army Group C. There you will meet Judge Advocate Dr Schröder, who will give you further instructions. We've attached one further condition to your release.'

'I hope it isn't something which forces me to refuse,' said Pastor Degenbrück.

'We're not asking much of you,' I said. 'It's merely that you shall go and stay with a German-Italian in Como until a favourable opportunity presents itself for you to escape to Switzerland.'

'I accept your conditions, Doctor, provided that the oper-ation can't get you into any trouble in any way. What happens if I'm arrested again and it turns out that I'm not suffering from the disease you've given me?'

'The disease from which you are suffering can't be diag-nosed objectively. If you indicate the symptoms skilfully enough no none will be able to fault you. Dr Schröder will be responsible for the rest, and he'll be covered by my certif-icate.' I had. Pastor Degenbrück taken out again. Then I took an official prison form and wrote:

'Medical Corporal Degenbrück has been complaining for some time from attacks of cramp in the region of the heart, accompanied by shortage of breath and sensations of anxiety. His heart, on examination, proves entirely normal.

Nevertheless, the attacks have increased in the last few days. He is suffering from *angina pectoris nervosa*. He is unfit for arrest at present and requires special treatment immediately. Dr Vossmenge, Major.'

Then I took the certificate together with the prisoner's personal file to Dr Schröder.

'If something unforeseen should happen, Doctor,' he said, 'I'll ring you up at your office in Malcesine. If the message is that the court needs you for the trial of Mayer II on a charge of self-mutilation, then you will be well advised to disappear at once. In that case you must fend for yourself.' 'I'm not often at staff headquarters,' I replied. 'You won't always be able to get me there. But I'm not afraid of our coup being discovered. In any case no one will be able to prove that the prisoner Degenbrück was not suffering from *angina pectoris nervosa* when I examined him. On the other hand, I don't quite see how you are going to be able to spin the case out indefinitely.'

'I sincerely hope,' said Dr Schröder, 'that the war will be over before I have to take up the case against Degenbrück again. I can put it off for a few months all right.'

I drove back to Malcesine.

It seemed that Medical Corporal Degenbrück was saved.

Chapter 37

I was arrested in Treviso at the beginning of November by order of the Senior Air Medical Officer and brought to the military prison in the Fort St. Mattia in Verona. The prison doctor enquired after my state of health but refused to answer my questions about the reason for my arrest. Eventually I was interrogated by a Colonel Clemenz of the court martial department of the General in Command of the Luftwaffe in Italy and learnt that this same prison doctor at St. Mattia had lodged a complaint against me to his superior officer. This was to the effect that I had encroached on his duties and had made out a certificate for the release of a prisoner without being in any way competent to do so. The complaint found its way through the regulation channels to the medical General at Army Group C who ordered me to be reprimanded for encroaching on the sphere of activities of an army doctor. This order was forwarded to the Senior

Air Medical Officer with the request that the background to my intervention should be looked into, for it was an unusual thing for a Luftwaffe doctor, and particularly a psychiatrist, so openly to disregard an army doctor's authority as to declare a prisoner awaiting trial unfit for arrest.

The Senior Air Medical Officer, who was subordinate to the medical General at Army Group C, ordered an enquiry. When Judge Advocate Dr Schröder suddenly disappeared— he is still wanted on a charge of desertion—the Senior Air Medical Officer began to suspect a plot. My arrest followed.

Colonel Clemenz's interrogations brought some variety into the monotony of daily life in St. Mattia. My cell, which had formerly been one of this Austrian Alpine fortress's powder magazines, was cold, damp and dark. The food was bad. The only time I saw any daylight was when I was brought up for interrogation. Colonel Clemenz read out the charges against me. These consisted of releasing a prisoner, favouring a prisoner and violating my duty—none of them offences which necessarily incurred the death penalty. Only if they succeeded in proving that I had known of Degenbrück's crime would a death sentence be inevitable.

The Colonel further revealed to me that in view of the heavy penalty I could expect I would be given a defence counsel with whom I could discuss everything quite openly. Captain Werle, a lawyer in civilian life, and now in charge of Luftwaffe despatches in Verona introduced himself to me as my defence counsel. He advised me to put the blame for everything on the missing Judge Advocate Dr Schröder. For the present the court martial was convinced that I knew nothing of the serious crime of which Medical Corporal Degenbrück had been accused. My counsel further informed me that the Field Marshal had insisted on my being punished as severely as possible, but there was a hope that he and his whole staff would be transferred to Vienna before my trial came on. If that was so my case would automatically be handled by the court martial department of the Luftwaffe General for Italy. I had nothing to fear from my old General. In order to gain time, he, Captain Werle, had applied to have me put under mental observation for six weeks in the psychiatric department of the Luftwaffe hospital in the Villa d'Este at Cernobbio near Como.

After four weeks' imprisonment at St. Mattia, I was transferred under heavy escort to the Villa d'Este on the shores of Lake Como. Here I was given a psychiatric examination by a medical Major, who had previously worked under me. Since it is pointless for one psychiatrist to try and examine another, I suggested that I should write down my experiences with Pastor Degenbrück. I shan't try and hide my acquaintance with Degenbrück from the court, for a lie like that is easily refuted. I will also openly admit that I knew of his crime. Besides, the writing will pass the time for the Field Marshal and his staff haven't moved to Vienna yet.

Chapter 38

THIS was where I had meant to bring these notes to an end. But I now have one last chapter to add:

On New Year's morning 1945 the door of my not uncomfortable prison opened and the guard said: 'Look out, doctor! *Kasak* coming!' *Kasak* was the word the troops used for Catholic priests—an abbreviation for *'Katholische Sündenabwehrfeanone*.'*

I went over to the door to meet the priest.

'*Permesso, Signore, sono venuto. Lei ha forse bisogna di me.*'

The voice seemed familiar.

'*Molto gentile, Monsignore,*' I answered. '*S'accomodi pure.*

---

* Sündenabwehrfeanone = Sin defence cannon, from *Flugzeugabwehrkanone* (Flak)

Su questa sedia, prego.'

I offered him the only chair in the room. He sat down. I sat down on the bed.

When the guard had shut the door on the outside my visitor said softly:

'Not *Kasak*. Wind Doctor, *Esak*[*].'

'Are you mad, Orange Pastor,' I said. 'If you're recognised, everything we've done for you will be in vain. I assumed you were in Switzerland long ago.'

'What you have done for me, Robert Vossmenge, can never be in vain—Christ says: "Inasmuch as ye have done it for the least of these my brethren, ye have done it unto me."'

'It wasn't to get credit for myself that I helped you,' I said.

'You have sacrificed yourself for me, Doctor,' said Pastor Degenbrück, 'but I'm not going to accept your sacrifice. You will immediately put on this soutane and stick on my false beard. I on the other hand will dress myself in the uniform of a Major in the Medical Corps and meet the fate I have so well deserved. I hope you'll respect the reasons for my decision. There's a blue Fiat standing outside in front of the hospital. It's a closed car and inside you will find Dr Schröder. He will drive with you to Menaggio to-day. From there an Italian guide will take you over by an unguarded route to Switzerland. This evening you will be safe in Lugano. Everything has been well prepared. Please don't make trouble. We haven't got much time.'

'I'm full of admiration for your tricks, Orange Pastor, but you obviously haven't realised that I'm taller and fatter than you. Your soutane wouldn't fit me. You don't think our disguise

* Esak = Evangelische (Protestant) *Sündenabwehrfeanone*

would take in the guard outside for a moment, do you?'

'Desperate measures are necessary, Doctor, I'm relying on your friendship.'

'And I on yours. Friendship is a reciprocal thing.' I said. 'Why don't you want to accept my sacrifice? Don't I seem worthy of it? From the very first day we met you've been trying to guide me onto the right path. I know I've been a lot of trouble to you. Are you going to give up now just when your efforts are at last bearing fruit? You don't want to stop me doing my first truly Christian action in the whole of my life, do you?'

'Oh my God, what am I to do? This wasn't what I meant. This was a development I couldn't have foreseen. But heaven will reward you for your good intentions. I can't accept your sacrifice.'

'Why use such big words, Orange Pastor?' I said. 'Everything that I am to-day I owe to you. Won't you let me show my gratitude?'

'What have I done that you should think you owe me gratitude? If your present knowledge of the truth makes you happy you owe that not to me but to Another Whose word I preach. I can't accept your sacrifice.'

'I'm not sacrificing myself for you, Kurt Degenbrück. Don't you understand?'

'Oh, my God, into what temptation hast Thou led me! What am I to do? Am I justified in preventing a man from becoming Your disciple? But what nonsense I'm talking! Doctor, I don't accept it. God does not require your sacrifice.'

'How are you so sure of that, Orange Pastor?' I said. 'Besides you're wrong when you suppose that the cynic of yesterday has turned into the religious fanatic of to-day. I'm not risking much. What is the sentence I have to expect? The penalty for freeing a prisoner isn't death. But you won't have a chance if you're found here. I've got other reasons too for insisting that you should get to safety and leave me here. I'm thinking of our future.'

'I don't understand you.'

'I'll explain then, but it's my last word to you. If you don't leave here as soon as I've finished, I shall call the guard. You can treat what I am now going to say to you as a genuine confession.'

'Oh, my God, this is too much! But go on.'

I said:

'The war will soon be over. We can hardly have any idea of what will happen to Germany then. This much is certain: there'll be need of men like you, Orange Pastor. There's not one Protestant pastor in a thousand like you. To-day, in the hour of our farewell, I can say that to you. Most pastors have studied theology for eight terms but have never studied life at all. They know the Bible by heart but of life itself they know nothing. Many pastors don't speak the language of people of to-day at all. And many of them don't even know the needs of the people to-day. Besides one doesn't credit many of them with any faith. All they seem to have is a knowledge of theological dialectics. They want to convert people wherever they go. They don't know how terribly difficult it is to believe. They drive intelligence out of the Church. They're only interested in old women who spend their time on their knees and people who go to Church on Sundays, as if praying and going to Church were the only signs of true Christianity.

'But you're not like that, Orange Pastor. I assume there must be more of your sort. Everything is going to depend on you in the future. After the war is lost, there'll be a great longing in Germany for grace and salvation in the Christian sense. If men are once more fobbed off with the usual theo-logical phrases, then the ravages of war will have passed over us in vain. So, it's not out of love for one of my fellow men but out of deep concern for our future that I have made my small contribution to your rescue.'

'And what about you, Wind Doctor? You'll be needed too.'

'I haven't got a clear conscience, Orange Pastor. Only someone who has openly opposed the Anti-Christ as you have always called Hitler in our conversations, only some-one whose conscience is as clear as yours can lead men out of their spiritual poverty when this war is over. I know noth-ing of politics. I don't even accuse myself of having made a political mistake. It's human to make mistakes. But I can never forgive myself that I have done nothing to oppose the inhuman cruelties of this authoritarian regime. On the other hand, though, I don't see what one could have done to com-bat the madness of our time. The individual was powerless. This dilemma causes me more suffering than I can say. I'm tired and I don't care what happens to me. My last wish is that you should survive this war. You have opened my eyes for me. To-day you see me truly penitent. And what remains to me at the end of this long night of wandering and madness? The realisation that all human activity is of doubtful value.'

Pastor Degenbrück made no reply. Then the guard came into the room. Pastor Degenbrück stood up.

'*Ego te absolve in nomine Patris et Filii et Spiritus Sancti,*' he said, and he made the sign of the cross over me. I kissed his hand. Then he left the room without a word.

Judge Advocate Dr Schröder and Pastor Degenbrück escaped to Switzerland where they found asylum for the rest of the war. As for Dr Robert Vossmenge, all of us who were concerned for his fate, hoped that he would be spared the worst in the forthcoming trial. The fudge Advocate-General of the Luftwaffe in Italy had appointed Judge Advocate Dr Hermann as Prosecutor. He couldn't have made a better choice. He intended to preside at the trial himself. To accompany him on the bench he appointed a Major from the General's staff and a doctor whose integrity was beyond dispute. The one personal enemy whom Dr Voss-menge had made for himself was not in a position to influence the trial, for the Field Marshal's staff was finally transferred to Vienna. Unfortunately, I wasn't able to help Dr Vossmenge with my medical report in the same way as he himself had helped others. There seemed every reason to suppose that the court martial would only give him a light sentence. But at the end of January a special commission equipped with full powers arrived from Berlin and set itself up over the head of the Judge Advocate-General's department. The trial of Major Dr Vossmenge lasted only two hours. None of our own judges was present at the trial. No experts were called. No prisoners' friend, or defence counsel was allowed. Major Dr Vossmenge was sentenced to death on the 2nd of February 1945. He was shot the next day in the moat of Fort St. Leonardo just above Verona. I haven't been able to find out where he is buried.

Afterword:
Being Disagreeable

by Chris Maloney

Between 1933 and 1945, around 360,000 German people – largely those diagnosed with mental disorder or an inherited disability – were forcibly sterilised as part of the National Socialist ('Nazi') regime's drive to cleanse German society of 'biological threats'.[1]

In September 1939, these Nazi attempts to remove disability from the gene pool intensified under the 'Aktion T4' programme. Designated doctors were authorised to select patients 'deemed incurably sick, after most critical medical examination' and administer a 'mercy death'.[2] An estimated 200,000 individuals diagnosed with mental disorders were put to death in this way. The German medical profession was central to the programme, and psychiatrists were amongst its most enthusiastic adopters.[3]

This is the background to Friedrich Deich's story of Dr Voss-menge, a young psychiatrist trained in the 1920's and 30's who falls foul of the regime and has to flee abroad. He later joins the German war effort, first in North Africa and then in Italy. Professionally isolated, he has to define for him-self what a psychiatrist is and should be. He faces his own dilemmas and tests, but, having been forced to leave Ger-many, he is spared having to decide whether he stands with, or against, his one-time colleagues, as they implement the programme of killings in his homeland.

How might we understand Vossmenge in the broader con-text? How do his experiences and choices relate to those of his creator? For the English reader and researcher, the author of *The Sanity Inspectors* is hidden behind veils of language, time, and a degree of deliberate concealment. Published in the US and UK in 1957, the book was never reprinted in Eng-lish, although it was reissued several times in the original German version (entitled *Windarzt und Apfelsinenpfarrer* – 'The Wind Doctor and the Orange Parson') and was translated into French as *Cahier d'un Psychiatre* in 1964. Until now, the English translation had almost disappeared without trace, with only occasional copies on the second-hand market.

Friedrich Deich was the pseudonym of Dr Friedrich Weeren (1907-1978), a German psychiatrist, journalist, and author. According to the biographical sketch on the 1956 dust jacket for *The Sanity Inspectors*, he was:

> born in 1907 and studied medicine at the Universities of Bonn, Freiburg and Munich. He later studied under Kutscher at Munich and then became assistant in Dr

Bumke's psychiatric clinic. In 1938 he was forced to give up his position for political reasons and travelled in Africa. He spent the war, as may be guessed from his novel, as a doctor in military service.

Dr Oswald Bumke, Deich/Weeren's teacher, was a great believer in the 'scientific' approach to psychiatry that Dr Vossmenge follows for much of his career. Bumke was a prominent psy-chiatrist and neurologist, a figure who courted controversy, challenging existing diagnostic systems. He advocated under-standing psychiatric syndromes through scientific methods – the approach that Vossmenge expounds so often to in his letters to the Pastor. Bumke had been part of a team of neurol-ogists summoned to Moscow to attend to Lenin in May 1923 following the Soviet leader's third stroke – a three-day trip that stretched into seven weeks as the doctors attempted, unsuc-cessfully, to save him. In 1924 Bumke was appointed Chair of the Psychiatry Department of the University of Munich, a post he held throughout the Nazi era. He was suspended from the position by the Allies in 1946, to undergo a denazification investigation, but reinstated the following year.

Friedrich Weeren, however, had moved on from his assistant's post well before that. According to his obituary, he was dismissed in 1938 for 'political unreliability'.[4] Records of German research funding locate him in the Research Centre in Stanley Poole in the Belgian Congo between 1938 and 1940, where he received seven tranches of funding to study 'West African forms of dengue [fever]'.[5] Like his protagonist Dr Vossmenge, Weeren then worked as a unit doctor and psychiatric expert with the Luftwaffe in North Africa and Italy, from 1941 to 1945.[6]

He returned to Germany after the war and started writing under the pseudonym Friedrich Deich. As Deich, he went on to have a relatively high profile in German journalism and comment up until the 1970's. He may also have had a psychiatric practice under his own name, but no information is available about this.

More biographical details can be gleaned from an item in the 'Personalia' section of the *Deutsches Arzteblatt*, the weekly journal of the German Medical Association, which noted Weeren's 65th birthday in February 1973. Writing under the name of Deich, he had been a science editor at *Die Welt* (founded in Hamburg in 1946 by the British occupying forces) and subsequently head of the science department at *Die Neue Zeitung (The New Times)*. *Die Neue Zeitung*, published in the American Occupation zone from 1945 to 1955, was considered by some to be the most important newspaper in early post-war Germany, with a wide range of influential contributors including Heinrich Boll, Bertolt Brecht and Max Frisch.

The novel *Windarzt und Apfelsinenpfarrer*, later translated as *The Sanity Inspectors*, appeared around the time Deich/Weeren's post at *Die Neue Zeitung* came to an end. He later published two other books, *Was Haben die Arzte uns heute zu sagen* ('What Doctors Have to Tell Us'), and *Ein Tag im Paradies* ('A Day in Paradise'), although neither were translated into English. He went on to serve as editor-in-chief of the medical journal 'Euromed', and to co-found the West German 'College of Medical Journalism'.[7] He wrote regularly for national newspapers, worked for the Deutschen Forschungsdienstes, the German Research Service, and received a number of prestigious professional awards.

In 1984, six years after Weeren's death, the 'Friedrich Deich Foundation' was set up by the Federal Association of the Pharmaceutical Industry ('BPI'), with a commitment to promoting science journalism 'in the interest of the transfer of scientific research results in the medical, pharmaceutical and health economic fields.' The Foundation generously dispensed prizes, bursaries and research funding up until 2002, when it was disbanded. Neither the BPI nor the Federal body that administered it, holds any record of links with Dr Weeren's family.

We learn about Dr Vossmenge's career through his own account, written whilst under the threat of court martial. But what we read has also been selected and précised by an unnamed narrator, himself also a character in this novel by Dr Friedrich Deich, who is in turn a creation of Dr Weeren, about whom we have little, if any, personal information. And it has all been translated by Robert Kee.

For now, let's take what we know of Vossmenge at face value. How closely his experiences and opinions match those of Friedrich Deich, or Dr Weeren, is a different matter

The young doctor we first meet is troubled by two ongoing conversations: one with his teachers, who view him as softhearted, and lacking clinical rigour; the other with Kurt Degenbrück, a hospital pastor, for whom he is the embodiment of the psychiatric establishment. In dialogue with these accusers, Dr Vossmenge starts to find his own way, as all psychiatrists in training must do if they're to fully engage with the difficulties of the work. In his accounts of conversations with his teacher Dr Stohr, Vossmenge describes how he came to study medicine and psychiatry, highlighting his belief in compassion and the need to understand the minds of others – tempered by clear observation, and an ability to think for himself.

At the time Vossmenge was training, German psychiatry was in a creative ferment. Emil Kraepelin, now widely viewed as a key figure in the development of 'scientific' psychiatry, had proposed new ways of looking at mental illness, considering the course of illness as well as the immediate symptoms. In 1899, after careful and lengthy research and observation, he delineated two major forms of illness, or insanity; dementia praecox, later termed schizophrenia, and manic depression – the basis of the major diagnostic systems currently in use. The next generation of doctors did not accept all his formulations, however. Oswald Bumke, who succeeded Kraepelin as Professor in Munich was one of his more outspoken critics. Despite (and probably in reaction to) the conceptual leaps of previous decades, the field was once more being redefined.

In this context, Vossmenge becomes steeped in the view of psychiatry as a science. As a dutiful student of this approach, his patients become subjects of scientific enquiry, and, to a lesser degree, classification. Their stories drive the early chapters of the book along, in parallel with his discussions with Pastor Degenbrück. In these discussions, it is Dr Vossmenge who takes the position of being wise in the ways of the mentally ill, in contrast with the pastor's apparent naïveté.

Both sets of conversations involve the questioning of formulations of sanity and madness that judge the beliefs of the individual in relation to those of the people around them – and herein lies the essence of the book. Some of these questions are played out in the cases, which raise questions that beset psychiatry to this day. How do we define madness? What are the risks of using social norms as the touchstone for sanity? Can we accept a pluralistic reality, and if so, would this still allow society to function? And how does the spiritual dimension relate to all of this? Some of the implications of psychiatric labelling are also explored: the social as well as purely 'medical' consequences that can both help and hinder. What may most strike some modern readers is the paternalism and the 'othering' of the patients. This was in so many ways the spirit of the age – yet there is a humanity in the encounters described that repeatedly cuts through it.

So far, so good... a nicely observed, thoughtful book, reminiscent of many popular works, written in an easy style... 'All Mad Folk Great and Small', akin to James Herriot's successful and well-observed tales of life as a provincial vet... But there is an accident of geography. This is 1930's Germany, not the Yorkshire Dales, and on 30th January 1933, Vossmenge's diary reads 'Elfie back from skiing. Gave Bunty [her terrier] back. Hitler Chancellor of the Reich.' The narrator remarks drily 'Robert had not quite overlooked it.'

Shortly after this, the psychiatric staff are informed they are to be 'transferred' into being members of the Nazi party. At the reception, however, Vossmenge makes a weak joke, mocking his colleagues' anti-Semitic statements. Two of the doctors have their membership turned down: the joker himself and the only one of his colleagues who laughed.

The role of the medical profession in the activities of the National Socialist regime has been the subject of considerable scrutiny and ongoing re-evaluation over the years. Here, a few observations will have to suffice to alert the reader to the context.

Dr Hartmut Hanauske-Abel, a paediatrician and medical researcher in the U.S., published a helpful collection of primary sources in 1996, in a special edition of the *British Medical Journal* (the British equivalent of the *Deutsches Arzteblatt*) commemorating the 50th anniversary of the start of the Nuremberg doctors' trials.[8] His paper, 'Not a slippery slope or sudden subversion', draws together material from the leading medical journals of the time and charts the responses of the profession to the new regime in 1933.[9]

Hitler was appointed Chancellor on 30 January of that year. In March, the *Deutsche Arzteblatt*, as the voice of the professional establishment, reported that Dr Alfons Stauder, the elected president of the two largest German medical associations, had telegraphed Chancellor Hitler to say that they 'gladly welcome the firm determination of the Government of National Renewal to build a true community of all ranks, profession and classes, and gladly place [ourselves] at the service of this great patriotic task.'[10]

So far, so anodyne. But by June 1933 the journal's title page carried the proclamation that the central promotional organisation of physicians and its Education Office 'have the purpose of enhancing the idea of racial improvement among physicians and within the population. In doing so the medical profession has unselfishly devoted its services and resources to the goal of protecting the German nation from biogenetic degeneration.' There were no signs of reluctance or circumspection – on the contrary, the author continued, 'The medical profession has a special responsibility to work within the framework of the state on the tasks posed by population politics and racial improvement.'[11]

The German medical profession was not alone in its interest in such measures at the time. In the early part of the century, Eugenics had developed as a popular concept and had broad support in science, medicine, and academia. Sterilisation programmes were openly proposed by such public figures as George Bernard Shaw and adopted in the 1920's and 30's in countries including Belgium, Brazil and Canada. Under the Nazis, however, Germany now had a regime with racial 'hygiene' as one of its fundamental objectives.

On 14 July 1933, the Sterilisation Act, or 'Law for the Prevention of Genetically Diseased Descendants' came into effect. Paragraph 12 instructed that the operation 'must be performed even against the will of the person to be sterilised. The attending surgeon must request any necessary assistance from the police authority. If other measures are insufficient it is permissible to use direct force.' Insurance companies and 'the one who has been sterilised' were to be billed for the operation. The law established a formal regime of genetic health, including appellate genetic health courts, attached to civil courts and presided over by a lawyer and two doctors, one of whom was an expert in medical genetics.

Psychiatric illnesses and alcoholism were included in the list of 'genetic illnesses', which doctors were obliged to register akin to any other 'notifiable' disease.[12]

In the first year of the Sterilisation Act, Germany's genetic health courts received 84,525 physician-initiated applications and reached 64,499 decisions, 56,244 in favour. Doctors competed to fulfil sterilisation quotas; sterilisation research and development rapidly became one of the largest medical industries. Within four years, almost 300,000 patients had been sterilised, at least half for 'feeble mindedness' as evidenced by failing 'scientifically designed' intelligence tests.[13]

In 1937, four years after being refused Party membership, Dr Vossmenge was still in post. With no sign of any greater interest in politics than before, when quizzed on a visit by Pastor Degenbrück he acknowledges having taken part in sessions of the Racial Hygiene Commission 'from time to time' as advisor or observer. The Pastor raises the spectre of euthanasia, invokes the Anti-Christ, and asks that God preserves us from psychiatry, but Vossmenge appears implacable. Their argument devolves into one about how 'pathological imbecility' may be detected and that the methods used were imprecise. Broader moral issues are left unaddressed.

Others shared the Pastor's concerns about an over-inclusive and possibly over-enthusiastic approach. In 1937 Dr Gerhard Wagner, a committed National Socialist, who had replaced Dr Stauder at the head of the profession, sent a memorandum to Hitler in which he cited 'the sterilisation of entire families whom providence did not give the chance to receive the degree of formal schooling that is required to pass the intelligence tests... Science has to remain the servant of our political principles and intentions.'[14]

Vossmenge's subsequent dogged and perhaps ill-judged pursuit of his own practice leads him into conflict with the local Party, and he decides to flee the country. It was only after this departure that the forced sterilisations were halted (largely for political reasons), giving way to the T4 programme in 1939. This was a nationwide, centralised, and peer reviewed process that directed the killing of adults and children clinically classified as 'futile' or 'terminal' cases. The programme was geared towards efficiency in healthcare and more careful use of limited resources. Vossmenge was not put to the test that so many of his colleagues faced, that of having to decide where he stood on all this, to declare his own priorities. Who knows what he might have thought or done?

The second part of the book concerns the madness of the German Army and Dr Vossmenge's struggles and compromises with his own sense of personal and professional integrity. He spends time as a medical officer in North Africa but is transferred to a Luftwaffe hospital in Rome just before the Afrika Korps' defeat. Here he develops his psychiatric expert practice and reports various examples of his capacity to cut through to the human reality beneath the 'case' in which he is involved. This appeals to certain of the officers under whom he serves. Speaking his mind at the appropriate time, and to the right people, he gains promotion and influence. This is helped by his being the only psychiatrist available – he has no similarly qualified colleagues to contradict him.

The rigid and self-defeating processes that beset the Army feature prominently, whilst the peculiarities of some of its members are subject to scrutiny. Vossmenge's implicit view is that it is difficult to condemn men for their own erratic actions when the organisation itself is either mad or stupid.

And with the reappearance of Pastor Degenbrück, allowing their theological discussions to resume, Vossmenge more actively undermines official orders and decrees. He uses his expertise instrumentally, and (at least to his own mind) scientifically – to achieve humane outcomes through arguments that embellish the professional perspectives he had been taught. Looking back at some of the stories told, however, his approach has some features of more modern practice: the 'bio-psych-social', and bio-psycho- socio-spiritual' models of care are not far from his (for the time) provocative formulations of why his patients behaved as they did – looking beyond the simply 'medical' or 'scientific' to understand human psychology.

The discussions between Dr Vossmenge and the Pastor take on a new intensity. If anything, Vossmenge becomes the more radical of the two. Their common frame of reference becomes more explicitly Christian. Pastor Degenbrück is then arrested for identifying Hitler as the Anti-Christ, which sets in motion the train of events that results in Vossmenge's execution. Around the same time Vossmenge gratuitously makes an enemy, who later gets the chance to help him on his way to self-sacrifice. By the final stages of the story, Dr

Vossmenge is actively undermining or resisting the system, and at last has to do this 'out in the open', to rescue his friend.

This is, after all, only a story. A story that starts and ends with Vossmenge going to his death, and with echoes of the larger Christian story that frames his discussions with the Pastor. Dramatically, it is a moving climax. But does resisting an unjust system have to be a heroic act of such mythic proportions?

One of the subtleties of the book is that we see how a young doctor, entering a conservative profession with a sense of mission and idealism, is first inducted into that profession, and then gradually reaches his own accommodation with it. He is finally able to use all he has learnt in order to put into practice the ideals and attitudes he set out with, but might well have lost along the way

Vossmenge found himself in unusual circumstances, yet, as has already been alluded to, these circumstances spared him the decisions he would have faced if he had remained in his home profession and been charged with implementing Aktion T4. We now view this extermination programme as abhorrent, but at the time, German psychiatrists raised few objections. Had he stayed in Germany, Vossmenge's professional choices would have been more 'ordinary', in that all his colleagues faced them too – but more morally pivotal in another.

So, what about his contemporaries who remained in mainstream German practice? What had happened to *their* pursuit of ideals, and their sense of moral purpose? Stepping back again to 1933, the German medical profession had been one of the most sophisticated in the world, with perhaps the most tightly codified system of medical ethics.[15] German doctors were in ongoing dialogue with their colleagues in other Western nations. All were grappling with the demands of both public health and the needs and care of the individual – and judging which to prioritise, and when. Public health measures, particularly in the fields of immunisation and infection control, had had a profound effect on the health of whole nations. Genetics was then a relatively new science, holding out great hopes for the future. 'Eugenics' did not have the negative connotations it does now – and as already noted there was an international movement that targeted 'population weaknesses' as part of a larger set of social and economic problems that needed attention. Germany already had a record of public health programmes that emphasised early detection of illness and the promotion of occupational health and safety. The country had adopted the doctrine of holistic medicine (*Ganzheitslehre*), which advocated not only the comprehensive (that is, both physical and spiritual) needs of the whole person, but also those of the whole society in which the person lived.[16]

The National Socialist regime took pride in its aim of making Germany a 'hygienic' state. Hitler was celebrated as the 'great doctor' of German society, and Nazism claimed to be rooted in 'applied biology.' National Socialism promised to cleanse German society of its corrosive elements—not only Jews and Communists, but also pollutants in the air and water, along with tuberculosis, homosexuality, and the 'burdensome' mentally ill. In the Nazi view of the world such maladies were put down to the 'false humanitarianism' of previous political regimes.[17] Doctors (apart from the Jewish ones, who gradually had their livelihoods, their homes, and in many cases their lives taken away) were not victims of this process, but enthusiastic participants, readily taking on the powers offered by the state to fulfil the promises of an orderly, hygienic, and healthy nation.

In *The Uses of Pessimism*, Roger Scruton identifies the 'unscrupulous optimist' as the character who believes that 'the difficulties and disorders of humankind can be overcome by some large-scale adjustment: it suffices to devise a new arrangement, a new system, and people will [thus] be released from their temporary prison into a realm of success.'[18] Constraints are disdained, and those who get in the way can be cheerfully sacrificed. Old compromises are no longer required.

A current of such unscrupulous optimism and enthusiasm runs through those documents from the German medical establishment gathered together by Hanauske-Abel. These are not the writings of people who believe they are doing evil. These are optimistic documents, full of hope for the future.

Before you can make a stand against wrong-doing, you have to realise that what's being done is wrong. This is particularly hard if all your peers are going along with it.

And here the Pastor was at an advantage over Vossmenge. At the outset, his system of values was not based on anything as abstract as 'science'. Instead, he simply asserted the value of the individual, and their personal, unique relationship with God. And crucially, these values were held and expressed equally strongly by many of his colleagues.

Any controversies within Psychiatry in the early 1930's were as nothing compared to the disagreements that beset Germany's established Protestant church. Fierce opposition to the newly founded Nazi-supporting Deutsche Christen (German Christian) movement was played out in the election of church officials. Hitler imposed a new round of church elections in 1933 and an overwhelming number of key positions then went to the Deutsche Christiens. This prompted the formation of the Pfarrernotbund (Pastors' Emergency League), which opposed the 'Nazification' of the church and particularly the introduction of the 'Aryan paragraph' whereby those of Jewish descent were to be excluded. Within weeks of its founding more than a third of German pastors had joined the Pfarrernotbund. Later, in November 1933 a rally of 20,000 Deutsche Christien supporters demanded the removal of the Old Testament from the Bible. Pastors and church officials of Jewish descent started to be removed from their posts.

The Pastors' Emergency League went on to become the Bekennende Kirche, or 'Confessing Church', opposing the Nazi Party's efforts to build a single, pro-Nazi German evangelical church. This substantial movement was opposed to the regime's ecclesiastical policy, rather than (at least overtly) its overall political and social objectives. The struggle was to keep the church's own organisational structures intact, and to preserve the independence of church doctrine, so that the Christian commandments were not subordinated to Nazi ideology.[19] The pastor would thus have had a ready fund of like-minded colleagues to identify with and draw upon. Vossmenge had to take a lonelier course.

Robert Vossmenge is an average sort of a man, subject to a series of fortunate and unfortunate events. One thing leads to another and, ultimately, to an experience of redemption. In the end, he makes his powerful affirmation:

> I know nothing of politics. I don't even accuse myself of having made a political mistake. It's human to make mistakes. But I can never forgive myself that I have done nothing to oppose the inhuman cruelties of this authoritarian regime. On the other hand, though, I don't see what one could have done to combat the madness of our time. The individual was powerless. This dilemma causes me more suffering than I can say. I'm tired and I don't care what happens to me... And what remains to me at the end of this long night of wandering and madness? The realisation that all human activity is of doubtful value.[20]

Here, Vossmenge is talking about much more than his experiences in the Army. He acknowledges his own capacity for complicity overall, despite his acts of disagreement, such as they were. A misplaced sense of humour and a blinkered fulfilment of his clinical responsibilities had estranged him from the Party and constrained his available courses of action. Then, a series of encounters led him to an unexpected position of influence, where he found he could covertly achieve certain ends. None of this had involved making a principled stand or having any sort of plan, and there was no grand gesture until the end, when he sent the Pastor away. He just kept making the sort of decisions that those who knew him might have expected him to make. He acted within character, as we all do.

But Vossmenge had still needed others to amplify his faint misgivings. Some of this amplification came from his fellow officers as he went about his daily work. Most crucial of all, however, was Pastor Degenbrück, himself secure in his dissent. Their conversations, begun many years before, allowed Vossmenge to attend to his own internal questions about his most dearly held beliefs, held long before his medical edu-cation. The German title of the book – literally, 'The Wind Doctor and the Orange Parson' – places their relationship at the centre of the novel, in a way that the English title, *The Sanity Inspectors* (despite its immediate appeal) does not.

Dr Hanauske-Abel's compendium of German medical writings from the Nazi era in the *British Medical Journal* was not his first paper on the theme. Ten years earlier, in 1986, whilst still working in Germany, he had published an article in *The Lancet* on the role of German doctors under National Socialism. Within two weeks, his sublicence to practice emergency medicine was withdrawn by the Kassenarztliche Vereinigung, the Association of Statutory Health Insurance Physicians, an organisation closely related to the Chamber of Physicians itself. It was only restored to him after a ruling by the German Supreme Court.

Deich's novel was first published in 1955, a mere 10 years after the defeat of Nazi Germany, and barely eight years after the last of the Nuremberg doctors' trials had ended. Professional sensitivities are likely to have been far higher than in 1986. The book is circumspect in many ways. It never criticises the German medical profession openly, although it does convey some sense of how it functioned under the Nazi regime – and the ways in which its members thought. Yet, whilst steering clear of so much, it finds its way to the heart of the matter.

What part did Deich/Weeren himself play in the medical profession's activities during the Nazi regime – and how closely did his life path follow that of his hero, Vossmenge? Clearly, he did not go to his death, in an act of self-sacrifice and reparation. But, from what we know of him, he did share the experiences of exile following a disagreement with the Party, and army psychiatric service.

Maybe he managed to use his role to subvert inhumanity, in the way Vossmenge did – or maybe the book is about how he would have liked to have done so, a form of wish fulfil-ment. Maybe he was well aware how his being in Africa and Italy had spared him some difficult moral choices. Maybe he shared Vossmenge's despair at having stood by and not done anything.

Deich is telling us a story, and stories matter. The Sanity Inspectors raises many more questions than it answers. But it does explain why the answers aren't simple, and for all its lightness of touch it confronts us with serious issues. The book's story, and its ultimate message are complex and not necessarily worked out to Vossmenge's (or even Deich's) credit. It is a compelling and thought-provoking story of what might have been, by an author who understands the psychology of both conformity and dissent.

Endnotes

1. Burleigh M. Death and Deliverance: 'Euthanasia' in Germany c. 1900–1945. Cambridge: Cambridge University Press; 1994.

2. Proctor, Robert N. (1988). Racial Hygiene: Medicine under the Nazis. Cambridge, MA: Harvard University Press.

3. Strous, Rael D (2010) Psychiatric Genocide: Reflections and Responsibilities Schizophrenia Bulletin vol. 36 no. 2 pp. 208–210.

4. Deutsche Arzteblatt (1978) 75 (36) A-2020.

5. https://gepris-historisch.dfg.de, a fascinating compendium of information.

6. Deutsche Arzteblatt op cit.

7. Deutsche Arzteblatt (1973) 70(7) A-447.

8. British Medical Journal 7 December 1996, Vol 313 issue 7070, available online at https://www.bmj.com/content/313/7070 . Contains a fascinating compendium of articles on what may go wrong with medicine, public health and medical research.

9. Hanauske-Abel, H. M. (1996) Not a slippery slope or sudden subversion: German medicine and National Socialism in 1933. BMJ 1996; 313 doi: https://doi.org/10.1136/bmj.313.7070.1453.

10. Hanauske-Abel op. cit.

11. Walder K. (1933) Aufklarungsamt fur Bevolkerungspolitik und Rassenpflege. Deutsche Arzteblatt **62**:255–7. Translated in Hanauske-Abel op. cit.

12. Hanauske-Abel op. cit.

13. Proctor R. N. (1988) Racial hygiene. Medicine under the Nazis. Cambridge: Harvard University Press, pp 95–117.

14. Proctor op cit.

15. Proctor, R.N. (2000) Nazi Science and Nazi Medical Ethics: Some Myths and Misconceptions. Perspectives in Biology and Medicine, 43:3 pp.335-346.

16. Seeman, M.V. (2005) Psychiatry in the Nazi Era. Canadian Journal of Psychiatry 50:218-225.

17. Proctor, R.N. (2000) op cit.

18. Scruton, R. (2010) The Uses of Pessimism. Atlantic Books p.17.

19. Benz, Wolfgang (2006). A Concise History of the Third Reich. University of California Press.

20. Deich, Friedrich, The Sanity Inspectors, p. 269

The Sanity Inspectors
By Friedrich Deich
Translated from the German *Windarzt und Apfelsinenpfarrer*
by Robert Kee

First published in this edition by Boiler House Press, 2022
Part of UEA Publishing Project
Windarzt und Apfelsinenpfarrer copyright © Friedrich Deich, 1955
Translation copyright © Robert Kee, 1956
Introduction copyright © Sinclair Mackay, 2022
Afterword copyright © Chris Maloney, 2022

Photograph of Friedrich Deich courtesy of Axel Springer SE
Corporate Archive/Simon. Use of the cover illustration by
Gerard Hoffnung is with the consent of the The Gerard
Hoffnung Partnership
Cover Design and Typesetting by Louise Aspinall
Typeset in Arnhem Pro
Printed by Imprint Digital
Distributed by Ingram Publisher Services, UK

ISBN: 978-1-913861-87-2